READER !

Get these three
BONUS TOOLS
that will help you implement the
9 strategies

1

Two to Four Week Transformation
10-Step Process Sheet
*10 Practical steps you can take
to cash-in on the secrets in this book
—on one page!*

2

Free Sample BiteFX Animation
*One of our most popular animations that may be
worth thousands to your practice!*

3

The 5-Minute Splint Presentation
*See the short presentation Dr. Rick Rogers uses
to generate at least $20,000 a month
for his practice!*

VISIT
www.bitefx.com/hero

Becoming Your Patients' Hero

9 Secrets for Creating Exceptional Trust and New Income for Your Dental Practice

Don Reid, DDS & Doug Brown

Foreword by Peter E. Dawson, DDS

ISBN: 978-1-7325127-2-6

Printed in the United States

Published by High Impact Short Books

High Impact Short Books is the publisher of a unique type of business
short book — the shook. Shooks are designed to be read in a single sitting
and help the reader solve a specific problem or gain insight on a specific
idea. We help entrepreneurs and business owners create shooks quickly
and without the pain associated with writing traditional business books.
Do you have an idea for a shook you would like us to consider? Visit
www.Shooks.us for details.

Book design by Michelle M. White

Praise for Becoming Your Patients' Hero

If a picture is worth a thousand words, then animations are worth that ten-fold and more! Understanding occlusion can be difficult and complex and communicating it to patients even more so. This wonderful book offers you a better way to gain patient trust, and ownership of their problems with the ultimate result in allowing you to provide the necessary treatment for a successful outcome. And don't overlook their offer to try BiteFX live!

Howard S. Glazer, DDS, FAGD, Past President,
Academy of General Dentistry, Columnist: Dental Economics

Now we finally have it. A succinct book that is useful for kindling an appreciation for the diverse ramifications of TM dysfunction. Read it, understand it, and reap the benefits. It will be time well spent.

Hugh Lamont, DDS, MSc, FRCD(C) Orthodontist

Becoming Your Patient's Hero is an incredibly well-written and thoughtful book created for the dental physician who wants to be so much more than a "tooth doctor". It is both encouraging and enlightening and I recommend it highly for anyone in the dental profession!

Hal Stewart, DDS, CEO: The Stewart Center for Minimally
Invasive Dental Medicine (Formally The Texas Center)

"Becoming Your Patients' Hero" is a tremendous inspirational resource for those whose goal is to positively impact and change lives every day! The visual graphics of BiteFX, the testimonials of world class clinicians, and the experienced insights of Don and Doug, will guide all who read it into greater success and significance for years to come!

DeWitt C Wilkerson, DMD, Senior Faculty/ Director of Dental Medicine,
The Dawson Academy, Past-President American Equilibration Society (AES),
Past-President American Academy for Oral Systemic Health (AAOSH)

I often tell dentists whom I mentor: "at least half of an occlusal equilibration is done in the consultation room". This well written, easy to read book is a testament to this observation, with numerous communication pearls.

Mike Racich, DMD Clinician, Author, Lecturer, Mentor, www.DrRacich.ca

Being a dentist I'm a member of a 'Caring profession' but all too often we don't have the time, or the skills, or the tools to show to our patients that we do care, not just about their teeth or even their mouth but about them as a whole person. This book helps to give you those skills and introduces a great tool in BiteFX that we can use to help explain to our patients that we understand about their problems, their needs and the solutions we can offer. I've used BiteFX for many years since I first came across Doug demonstrating at the annual American Equilibration Society Meeting. It works both for my patients and for teaching Occlusion and TMD on behalf of the British Society for Occlusal Studies.

I love the idea of being able to say to my patients "This is what we're looking at and this is why we're looking" then straight into the appropriate BiteFX animations. It saves so many words and possible confusion. You can see it in your patients' eyes - that Lightbulb Moment of understanding that says, "Finally I've found someone who knows about my problems and how to fix them".

Mark Hargreaves, BDS LDS DGDP Teaching Programme for the British Society for Occlusal Studies (www.bsos.org.uk), Former Board Member AES

As a lab owner and busy technologist, I function as a valued source in the treatment planning process with my dentist clients. Having the book under my arm allows me to recall the stories within to help strengthen our planning and resolve for the patient. This book could not have come at a better time to supplement my own copy of BiteFX software.

Steve Killian, CDT, President Killian Dental Ceramics, Inc., CDL, www.killiandental.com

Every tool that enhances the ability of an individual to understand and own his or her present condition is a valuable addition to every dentist's tool box. ONLY patients who understand they have a problem can ask for a solution. BiteFX is an unparalleled experiential tool in the co-diagnosis of occlusal, joint, and muscle disease, it helps them ask.

Gary M. DeWood, DDS, MS, past Clinical Director at The Pankey Institute,
past Director of Curriculum and Clinical Education at Spear Education,
currently Executive Vice-President at Spear Practice Solutions,
always appreciator of Don and Doug's efforts to help me
connect with patients (and dentists). www.speareducation.com

I pride myself on trying not to be another "CE Junky". I always strive to implement what I learn. BiteFX along with this great book have helped me to implement all the things I've learned over the years by helping to simplify the complexities of occlusion to my patients.

Michael Monokian, DMD, www.monokiandentistry.com

Don and Doug have done it again!
BiteFX is the greatest tool available to help demystify the complexities of occlusion for our patients. The wonderful animations provide the patient with an understanding of where they are, how they got there and what can be done to bring them back to health.
This easy to follow book will provide every practitioner with an insight of what works and what doesn't. The stories told by doctors will help the reader find a better approach to getting the message out without "Muddying" the waters and overwhelming the patient. Knowledge gained through years of training is often stuck on a shelf with no clear way of putting it to use. Put down your pen and paper and let BiteFX help you dust off that knowledge and Become your Patients' Hero.

Gayle J. Fletcher, DDS, PA

This book is extremely helpful in many ways.

First, it helps the dentist understand occlusion better. This is the key to being an exceptional dentist because it allows for a level of diagnosis and treatment planning that too many dentists lack.

The second critical way that it helps is in helping our communication with our patients relative to occlusion and occlusal therapy.

I would highly recommend this book to every practicing dentist.

> ***Glenn E. DuPont**, DDS, Lead Faculty at The Dawson Academy,*
> *Past President of The Florida Academy of Dental Practice Administration,*
> *Past President of The American Academy of Restorative Dentistry,*
> *Past President of the Pinellas County Dental Association*

The first step along the pathway to becoming a master dentist is to acquire the knowledge and skills to solve the orofacial problems of our patients that are related to occlusion of the teeth. The second step is acquiring communication skills to enable patients to understand their problems and accept treatment. Knowing what you can do to bring comfort and health to your patients is one thing but enacting your vision is quite another. This little book "Becoming Your Patient's Hero" tells the stories of master dentists who travel this path daily. Stepping out of your comfort zone and enacting your vision of creating optimal oral health is good for your patient and it is good for you! This book and the BiteFX demonstration videos that accompany it can help you enact your vision.

> ***Jay Harris Levy**, DDS*

As the course director of Occlusion and TMD, I use BiteFX animations routinely to help my students understand basic concepts and could not imagine not having this valuable tool. This book will be a recommended read to my students!

> ***David Maddy**, DMD, Clinical Assistant Professor,*
> *University of Louisville Dental School*

BiteFX is one of the best tools we have, to have our patients see and value the occlusal correction services we can provide for them. This book explores many great ideas to that end.

Steven M. Hart, DMD, MAGD, Visiting Faculty, The L.D. Pankey Institute

BiteFX was a transformational component of my teaching and lectures. I really could not imagine having it taken away and going back to using stick figures and finger puppets to explain occlusal concepts. I will never be able to thank Don & Doug enough for that.

When I read "Becoming Your Patients' Hero", I just had to smack myself in the forehead. I cannot believe the opportunity and resource that I have been missing using it with my own patients. This book is a roadmap and recipe to easily implement an educational well source. Monday morning is going to be different at Lyme Road Dental!

Michael J. Melkers, DDS, MAGD (Master, Academy of General Dentistry), Founder Dr. Melkers' Seminars, Visiting Faculty, The Pankey Institute, Visiting Faculty, Riga Stradins University, www.MichaelMelkers.com

THANKS!

This is a short book, but you'd be surprised (we're surprised!) at how many people have been involved in its creation! So . . . sincere thanks to:

Mike Capuzzi (of High Impact Short Books, High Impact Marketing, and Copy Doodles fame www.mikecapuzzi.com) who suggested we write the book and mentored us through the process.

Dr. Peter Dawson for writing the perceptive foreword—it is always a pleasure and a lesson in graciousness working with you.

Everyone who shared their stories: Dr. Alain Aubé, Dr. Alan Blondman, Dr. T.J. Bolt, Dr. Kelley Brummett, Dr. Ian Buckle, Dr. Eric Farmer, Dr. Joe Gaudio, Dr. Brian Gray, Dr. Rick Rogers, Dr. Dennis Stiles.

Everyone whose comments on BiteFX® were included: Dr. Alain Aubé, Dr. Janet Burthem, Dr. Peter Dawson, Dr. Margareta Gavrila, Dr. Mike Schuster, Dr. Hal Stewart, Dr. Chris Toomey.

Everyone who reviewed this book and sent us their kind comments: Gary DeWood, Glenn Dupont, Gayle Fletcher, Howard Glazer, Mark Hargreaves, Steve Hart, Steve Killian, Hugh Lamont, Jay Levy, Dave Maddy, Mike Melkers, Mike Monokian, Mike Racich, Hal Stewart, Witt Wilkerson.

All the dentists on our mailing list who helped select the book's title.

All the members of Mike Capuzzi's High Impact Marketing Mastermind Group who willingly contributed comments and suggestions over several meetings: Dom Cassone, Mario Conlin, Dr. Kevin Flood, Jeff Giagnocavo, Michael Gray, Frank Lombardo, Mickie Kennedy, Brian Mittman, Bill Parlaman, Jon Toy, Fred White.

The faculty and leaders of the many continuing education organizations who have encouraged us along the way to equip dentists like you become heroes: The Pankey Institute, The Dawson Academy, OBI, The Stewart Center for Minimally Invasive Dental Medicine, The Canadian Occlusion Institute, British Society for Occlusal Studies, The Schuster Center, Spear Education, Clinical Mastery Series, Foundation for Advanced Continuing Education.

Ben Brown for giving support and input throughout the project and putting in place related webpages, emails and campaigns.

Stu Harman for keeping BiteFX sales, support, and coaching running so smoothly that huge chunks of time could be devoted to this book.

Michelle M. White for an outstanding job of copyediting, layout, and cover design.

Finally, those we appreciate the most: Doug's wife Liz and Don's wife Marilyn for your constant loving support in all we do!

Contents

PART 1
ATTITUDES, MINDSETS, AND APPROACHES

PART 2
TIMING, PRESENTATION TOOLS, AND TECHNIQUES

PART 3
BRINGING THE STRATEGIES TO LIFE

PART 4
PUTTING IT ALL TOGETHER—THE NEXT STEP

ABOUT THE AUTHORS

Foreword
by Peter E. Dawson, DDS

Dr. Peter Dawson

For many years Doug Brown has been a valuable resource I have relied on for animations that help me and the faculty at the Dawson Academy for Advanced Dental Study explain the complexities of occlusion. The work he has done in developing understandable animations of how the TMJ is designed to work and function has been invaluable in teaching dentists what they need to know (but typically do not know) about the relationship between the temporomandibular joints and the occlusion.

Dr. Don Reid stood out to me from early in his attendance at the Dawson Academy as one who loves to communicate with others. It was, therefore, no surprise when a few years later, he brought Doug and the animations they'd developed to me, explaining how these were transforming his ability to communicate occlusion to his patients. Despite being a great communicator, Don had recognized the need for a better visual tool to help his patients understand and accept what was best.

There is no doubt that the "secrets" Doug and Don talk about are some of the most important requirements dentists need to know to practice predictable dentistry. The authors are correct in calling them "secrets" because, despite their importance, most dentists are not even aware that they need to understand these essential principles.

I have often said that the best a dentist can be is mediocre if he or she does not understand how the occlusion must function in harmony with stable, healthy TMJs. That means every practicing dentist must have a working knowledge of how the TMJs function, and every dentist who works on teeth must be able to diagnose if there is any deformation or dysfunction within intracapsular structures of the TMJs before they start making changes to an occlusion. Even the anterior teeth are dependent on proper position and condition of the TMJs if the anterior teeth are to remain stable over the long term.

One of the greatest mysteries is why the most common cause of dental disorders, orofacial pain, and general dissatisfaction with dental treatment is ignored in all but the most exceptional dental school educations. Occlusal disharmony is responsible for a constellation of common dental problems, including excessive tooth wear, fractured cusps, sore teeth, and the most common cause of pain in the teeth, joints, and muscles, (occluso-muscle pain.) Yet, our extensive experience with thousands of dentists is clear: it is rare for dental graduates to be trained in the causes and effects of occlusal disease.

It has been our passion at the Dawson Academy to help thousands of dentists understand the important principles that make dental practice predictable and joyful. Doug Brown has been a partner in that effort by providing animated teaching aids that make complex subjects understandable. I must say that everything a dentist must know to be successful is understandable if the proper curriculum is provided.

The greatest joy of our faculty is to see the excitement and enthusiasm that is so common when dentists understand for the first time what they had been led to believe was too complicated for them to incorporate into their practices.

The learning process does not stop with understanding the principles. Dentists must be able to communicate these principles to their patients. BiteFX has been one of the most useful methods we have advocated for helping dentists explain their treatment plans in a way that patients can understand and accept what is needed. The combination of knowing how to solve patients' problems plus knowing how to explain treatment is a sure bet for success in any dental practice.

Don Reid has used this combination to build one of the most successful practices in a two-chair office in Tahoe. I'm grateful he is willing to share his experience in this easily read text—along with the excellent stories from so many top-notch dentists. I compliment both Don and Doug for their notable contribution.

Why We Wrote This Book for You

Dr. Don Reid

From Don

I had no idea that when I began treating patients in 1975, I'd entered a profession that would provide me an opportunity to impact people physically, personally, and spiritually beyond my earliest wild imagination.

My purpose in writing this book is to share pearls of wisdom acquired from family members, dentists, dental clients, psychologists, philosophers, friends, and fishing buddies, whom I cherish and enjoy daily, in practice and in life.

The purpose of my practice is to enable clients, using clear and simple communication, to grasp what it takes, from our doctor-client relationship, what 'we' need to do to maintain a healthy, comfortable, and functional mouth for a lifetime.

I didn't set my goals as a young dentist to be an expert in any particular area of dentistry or to be an author or a teacher. It just happened. My goal was to be the best that I could be, given all of my human frailties, and to have an open mind to listen and learn from my mentors that achieved remarkable practice success, great family lives, and balanced lifestyles. Common to all my dental mentors was a deep underlying passion to offer the best treatment, not push or sell dentistry, to forgive people for the shame and guilt they carry for years of neglect, and to care more about patients' lives and wellbeing than getting instant case acceptance.

Understanding occlusion was a huge 'game changer' for me. Understanding how clients feel and think about dentistry and what motivates them was a similar big 'game changer'.

Early on, emotionally difficult patients and difficult mouths taxed me to the hilt, psychologically and technically. Now, I welcome these opportunities and look forward to the most difficult types of people and the most difficult oral problems.

Glimpses of why and how this paradigm shift happened are in these pages. I hope my insights are helpful.

From Doug

Doug Brown

About 15 years ago I had a vision for helping people understand concepts by taking the visualizations of experts and putting them into animations. Little did I know then that the main realization of that vision would be in dentistry!

Hundreds of dentists around the world have found the BiteFX program that we developed hugely impactful to their practices, and many of those teaching occlusion in dental schools and CE are choosing our animations to teach new generations of dentists these vital concepts.

It has been a big thrill to hear dentists tell us "BiteFX paid for itself in the first few hours" or "My practice has grown by 25% because of BiteFX." Yet . . . there are those who say, "I'm just not using BiteFX much" or "I don't see many occlusal problems" (surprising comment when others tell us 80% or more of their patients have occlusal issues).

I've had to accept that BiteFX can only work its magic when dentists have some other relational skills in place. These skills or strategies are useful for all dentists but have an explosive effect when combined with BiteFX.

Those who have this combination of skills and tools tell us they experience amazing results—which we tried to convey in the title and subtitle of the book.

- Too many dentists are missing one or more of the necessary skills—so they are "secrets" to them that need to be revealed.
- The skills revolve around occlusal disease - the most undiagnosed dental disease. Because it is the most undiagnosed, rich rewards are available to those who take it on.
- From the early consultation stages through initial relief of symptoms to long-lasting treatments and beautiful smiles, these dentists experience sincere and enthusiastic thanks from their patients.
- They become their patients' hero.
- They inevitably see significant new income as a result.

I'm the writer/editor of ***Becoming Your Patients' Hero.*** Don provided the core material, and I interviewed all the other dentist contributors (apart from Dr. Dawson who wrote the foreword himself) and wrote up their stories, which they reviewed and we edited to their satisfaction.

I've helped to put this book together in the hope that one or more of the secrets it shares will make the difference in making you a hero in your patients' eyes—so you regularly hear their thanks for your care, clarity, and time, and you can enjoy the resulting income growth.

The Big Idea Behind This Book

Knowing how to communicate occlusion to your patients is a vital part of giving them the best dentistry you can deliver.

Patients understand that decaying teeth need to be treated and can see periodontal issues developing. They'll demand treatment for acute pain!

However, when it comes to occlusion you are taking them into unfamiliar territory involving signs and symptoms they may not see, feel, nor connect with the health of their teeth. They probably haven't heard other dentists talk about occlusion nor had examinations that checked their occlusal health.

Over the years of equipping dentists with visual tools that help communicate unfamiliar occlusal concepts, we have observed common strategies being employed by those who are most successful in integrating occlusal treatment into their practices. While having excellent animations eradicates the problem of "the blank stare" (the dreaded lack of response when patients just don't get an attempted explanation of their occlusal issues), high occlusal treatment acceptance rates depend on combining other skills and strategies.

While obvious to some, these strategies *are secrets to many*—secrets that are preventing them from making the most of the skills they have learned.

This book reveals these strategies, amplifying them with examples from many dentists who employ them day-in and day-out.

The results of applying these strategies are:

- Your patients respect you more
- They trust you more
- Patients know you are different from other dentists
- That you have expertise that can help them in ways others have not been able to do
- Patients take ownership of their dental problems
- Patients ask you for solutions to the problems they can't manage themselves
- They give you permission to provide them with the best treatment you can deliver and which they can afford
- You have the opportunity to relieve them of any pains, discomforts, and other symptoms of occlusal disease and to go on to give them confidence-inspiring, beautiful smiles

In short, you become their hero!

We pray that a strategy, a story, a tip, or an attitude conveyed in this short book will open up this hero experience for you!

How an Understanding of Occlusion Transformed Don's Dentistry
and
How Learning to Explain Occlusion Transformed His Practice

While serving with the Marines in Vietnam, I had three teeth removed before I went into combat as a 'preventative' (Military-Intelligence!) approach to ensuring I wouldn't need a root canal while serving there. I remember well how difficult the extractions were. They were sound teeth, but my lifelong sugar habits caused their demise.

From the time I served until I arrived at dental school, eight years later, my occlusion changed drastically and I was the poster child at Temple Dental for severe tooth wear!

My quest to solve my own destructive pattern led me to explore nearly every occlusion philosophy known to man and kept me from attempting to restore anterior teeth on my patients with signs of wear for fear they'd be spitting out chards of glass routinely. I wanted to have my 'half-size' front teeth restored too but knew I'd have a similar fate.

I attempted trigger point injections, applied kinesiology muscle testing, neuromuscular dentistry, enumerable splint designs and gnathology, only to encounter mixed and unreliable results. I sometimes felt I was experimenting with patients. Experiments should be done on lab creatures not people.

Nearly ready to throw in the towel on another approach to occlusion in 1992, I responded to a mailer from the Dawson Academy. My fear was that this was going to be a treatise on how cusp tips and fossae interdigitate (which was the most painful exercise imaginable undertaken in dental school) but there were some items about the course content that intrigued me. I asked Steve Killian, my lab guy and lifetime friend, to attend the seminar with me. Much to our surprise, Steve and I witnessed Pete Dawson using simple stick-like drawings of the TMJ system so simple a fifth grader could understand. I knew he was explaining the answers I was searching for. The fog that had surrounded "occlusion" for me cleared. Not only could I see what I'd been doing wrong but there was a method I could use to make things right in the future.

The following Monday, a patient came in with a fractured beautiful four unit bridge. When I allowed his mandible to go where I now felt it belonged; the only contact was on that bridge, precisely where the failure occurred!! I told him: *"I have good news and bad news. The bad news is you broke this very strong and esthetic new bridge. The good news is I know why this happened and I can fix it so it won't occur again."* I picked up a large diamond burr and equilibrated that fractured area until both sides of his teeth touched at the same time while maintaining his condyles in a seated jaw position. That was the first time I heard a patient say. *"Wow! What did you do? That feels awesome."*

I still had much to learn, so in the following decades I continued to study different aspects of occlusion with more in-depth Dawson classes, Spear seminars and different study clubs, but from that point forwards, I saw declining failures and spectacular, life-changing successes.

Other technical skills have made significant differences, but it has been the understanding of occlusion that has provided me with the foundation for my clinical success.

There was still another hurdle I had to overcome before my practice took off to the stratosphere, at least the stratosphere that I enjoy, which is that of doing high-end, full-mouth, challenging reconstructive work, supported by implants, three days of the week.

I've always related well with people and, I'd say, exude a fair amount of confidence. Teaching from Drs. Omer Reed, Robert Barkley, Earl Pound, and psychologists Bud Ham and Chuck Sorensen, early in my career equipped me with the tools and approaches that helped me connect with my patients and have them accept my treatment recommendations a good proportion of the time. Many of the lessons learned from these masters underlie the lessons you'll learn from this book. However, when it came to occlusion, I often ran slap bang into the dreaded enemy: **the blank stare!**

I had a great box of tools to help me get the points across: the brilliantly engineered TMJ Tutor, a model skull with springs for muscles, the patient's models mounted in an articulator, and a good hand at making sketches. These all helped, but I felt I needed something more.

That's why I leapt at the opportunity when a friend, Doug Brown, asked me if computer animations could help me in my practice.

Today I can look back and see that **occlusion transformed my dentistry**, but it was **learning how to communicate this to patients** in ways they related to and that set them up to make the emotional decision to proceed with the recommended work **that really transformed my practice.**[1]

Without this visual explanation ability, enhancing my ability to communicate, I wouldn't be doing the high-end, highly productive, work I do, supporting a lifestyle here in the Lake Tahoe area that most would envy on just three days of work a week.

---

[1] While looking up a quote from Dr. Gordon Christiansen referenced a little later, we were interested to read the following conclusion to his article. It seemed so relevant to Don's experience and to the opportunity in front of you now, that we should include it here:"When practitioners become aware of the potential for service available to their patients by incorporating occlusal therapy into their practices, their entire vision of practice changes. Occlusal procedures become commonplace. Patients receive treatment not offered before, the dental staff is motivated and rewarded by learning the new procedures, and the practice generates more income."

This was true in 2002 and remains true today.

How Explaining Occlusion Transformed Dr. Joe Gaudio's Practice

Dr. Joe Gaudio, Chester, NJ

I suspect that at least the start of my story will be familiar to many.

After graduating as a dentist (I also did a concentration in prosthodontics in my final year), I set up a general practice that evolved over time to have a cosmetic focus. Crown and bridge were a staple of my daily work, and I applied all the principles I had been taught to the best of my ability.

Generally, things went well, but, **too often for my liking, something would go wrong that had me scratching my head.** It was obvious that I was missing a piece of the puzzle, but I didn't know what it was. Raising a family and paying the kids through college caused me to keep on putting off thoughts of searching for that missing piece.

Another factor that didn't sit comfortably with me was that a consulting group I was using to help me enhance my practice was telling me that I needed to instill a sense of urgency with my patients so that they would schedule treatment right away. It sounded good when they said it, but when I tried putting it into practice, it felt wrong. **The more I pushed, the more resistance I felt from my patients.** The consultants told me I wasn't executing the approach correctly, so I kept on trying, but it didn't feel good—too much like a slick salesman.

Providentially, shortly after my youngest child graduated, I saw John Cranham and Drew Cobb give a presentation in Baltimore. That was an eye opener! It was like I had been working in a dimly lit studio and someone came in and started turning on the studio lights—Boom! Boom! Boom!—with each insight Drs. Cranham and Cobb shared, another light came on, and I could see more of what had previously been hidden or mysterious to me.

It didn't take me long to sign up with The Dawson Academy and learn how one could actually put these new insights into practice. **Finally, I had the missing piece of the puzzle** and no longer felt I was taking a risk with every new case because I didn't know if it would hold up or not; I had control and saw predictable results.

Back at the office my staff weren't quite as enthused as I was by this latest set of changes I was bringing back from "yet another" CE course, but at least I knew I was heading in the right direction.

I received a bonus from The Dawson Academy when I heard Pete Dawson and John Cranham describe how they **patiently explained options to patients**—no pressure, just help the patients understand and opt for the appropriate treatment when they are ready. That was an approach I liked and was starting to see some success with.

I'd like to say that my practice was totally transformed at this point, but it wasn't.

I had the technical know-how to solve patients' chronic pain or tooth problems and deliver long-lasting dentistry, plus a way of talking to patients that felt right, but I still had two major stumbling blocks:

1. Part of the "no pressure" approach involved the patients understanding their needs, so they could make those informed decisions when they were ready. However, my determined, and unfortunately long-winded, efforts to explain to them the relationships of TMJs to teeth to muscles and the important geometries that protect teeth and other factors, were driving patients away.

2. My staff weren't totally on board with the "occlusal transformation" I was trying to bring about—not least because of what they saw me doing in point 1!

I don't like to think how things would have gone had a colleague not suggested I try BiteFX.

First, I showed my staff the basics—what a healthy bite looks like, why anterior guidance is important, how the muscles and TMJ work, and then how things go wrong when there are interference effects or deteriorating TMJs. I could see the light bulbs flashing on in their heads! No longer was I "crazy Dr. Joe off on his latest fad"!

Then, I found that sharing that same information with my patients, with just a few animations, made all the difference! I wasn't driving them away, and the no pressure approach started to deliver results far beyond what I'd ever seen. Just one example is that my Invisalign acceptance rates tripled!

Dr. Joe Gaudio, Chester, NJ

Now my staff, particularly my hygienist, Anita, tell me they do a better job of explaining occlusion to our patients than I do—and I'm delighted they think that.

I didn't realize I had quite so much to learn, but now that I have **a solid understanding of occlusion, a way of talking with patients that feels right and works,** and **visuals that enable me to implement what I know,** I am proud to say my practice has undergone a complete transformation.

Comparing how it was just a few years ago to where we are now is like comparing night to day. I'm enjoying my dentistry more than I ever had before and look forward to each new day. I'm also an annoying zealot in the AEGD residency program at Columbia University where I help weekly, but I think they appreciate the piece of the puzzle I'm providing!

I hope that, like me, you'll find that just one or two of the secrets in this book enable you to complete your own personal or practice transformation.

PART 1

Attitudes, Mindsets,
and Approaches

Some of these are general and apply to all your dentistry,

*Some are fundamental and may require profound
rethinking of your approach,*

And some are tweaks that you can quickly learn and apply.

1.
Communicating "I Care"

Do you care about your patients?

. . . Really care—in terms of wanting the best for their overall health and wellbeing?

Whether they voice it or not, knowing that you care about them is the #1 motivator for your patients to respond positively to your recommendations, come back to you in years to come, and refer friends and family to you.

You probably wouldn't be a dentist if you didn't care about improving people's health, so you might think this a dumb question—but the question is really:

How well do you communicate that you *don't* care?

- Do the pressures of your schedule make you so short and to-the-point that your patients have little chance to see that you care?
- Are you the technical expert, one who likes the protection of a formal doctor-patient relationship?
- Do you shy away from explaining a treatment plan because you're frightened of the rejection or feel that you would overwhelm the patient if you told them everything you felt they needed?

Any of these behaviors can say "I don't care" to your patients.

Explaining Occlusion Well Says, "I Care"

Of course, communicating that you care applies to all aspects of your dentistry not just the people that have occlusion problems, BUT what I love is that when I communicate occlusion well, my patients hear that I really care about them.

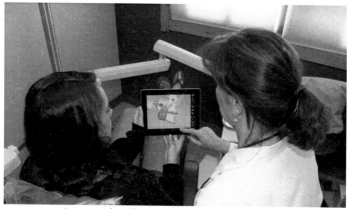

A personal explanation of occlusion says "I care"

Most occlusion problems don't hurt— yet. Patients might not yet have sore muscles; they might not yet have sensitive teeth. As their doctor, it's still my responsibility to tell them if I see signs of future problems.

If you went to a dermatologist and he saw a little melanoma, would he ignore it?

I sure hope not —if he does, get another dermatologist!

Occlusion problems are everywhere and patients have never been given the opportunity to understand what their problem is.

I explain to them that the signs I see they won't feel, but that those signs will most likely turn into symptoms if we don't figure out a plan to solve the future problem.

It's really easy to communicate because I believe it with all my heart and soul!

Why Explaining Occlusion Says, "I Care"

- I'm giving them respect by acknowledging they might want to understand their underlying issues.
- Taking some of my time to explain the key concepts says, "I care."
- They see I'm an expert in an important area ignored by other dentists—which again says, "I care for your best."
- They see I'm equipped to handle occlusion issues—why would I do that if I didn't want the best for them?
- When they understand how important it is for them to have a good occlusion and the several factors that support a good occlusion, they again hear, "I want the best for you."

Even if you have an extreme case of "hide-behind-the-doctor-mask" syndrome, and don't want to open yourself up to the touchy-feely things usually associated with communicating "I care for you", you can see that a few minutes opening your patients' eyes to occlusion might do the job for you!

Dr. Rick Rogers, of Fredrick, MD, is typical of many BiteFX members in saying:

"We hear patients tell us all the time how grateful they are to have found a dentist who can clearly explain their condition and show why the recommended appliance will have a positive impact on their symptoms."

Patients saying, "thank you" to a dentist for explaining their [occlusal] condition to them obviously know that Rick cares for them![2]

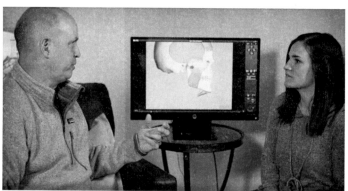

Dr. Rick Rogers demonstrating how he explains occlusion—
see his 5 minute video included in your welcome bonus
(see page i)

---

2   While at a mastermind group in Truckee, Dr. Rogers kindly demonstrated how he chats with a patient after his exam—you can see the video of Dr. Rogers as part of the welcome bonus described on the first page of this book.

Sadly, we turned the video off too soon as, Sam, our stand-in patient, who hadn't seen or heard anything Dr. Rogers shared with her before, jumped up as soon as we stopped recording and exclaimed, "That was fantastic!" – not the usual reaction one expects from patients when they hear explanations of dental concepts!

Every dentist needs to experience such positive reactions!

Strategy in Action— Communicating I Care!

Kelley Brummett, DMD,
Newnan, GA
Serves on the Board of Directors
of the Pankey Institute and Visiting
Faculty for the Essential 3 Course

Dr. Kelley Brummett

Gaining Trust

For me, one of the most important factors in my dentistry is my relationship with patients.

My technical skills enable me to help them improve their health across the many bodily, and often psychological, dimensions we influence, but unless I establish a solid relationship with my patients, gaining their trust, they're not going to give me the permission I need to proceed, nor will they gain the understanding they need to take ownership of their dental health.

A good example of this is nurse Sally, whom I've been working with for several months.

Sally has a class II bite, with classic features such as a double chin, some occlusal issues along with a habit of clenching. She's been to the orthodontist who recommended surgery, and my plan was to address the occlusal issues after the

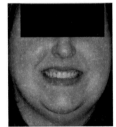

Patient "Sally"

surgery, but she's opted not to go for the surgery. Post orthodontics, we established occlusal splint therapy, but she fell out of the habit of wearing it during a recent pregnancy when she would frequently feel nauseous.

Sally returned to me recently complaining of severe pain in the upper right of her mouth. She has an impacted wisdom tooth on that side and was convinced that was the problem. There was slight swelling on the right side of her face. Palpation revealed that her masseter was on fire leading me to believe the pain was muscular in nature, not connected to the wisdom tooth.

However, to be sure, I took an X-Ray which showed nothing obvious in the area of the wisdom tooth, and I sent Sally to an oral surgeon to rule out any other issues outside of the muscle tension I was anticipating. He confirmed my diagnosis.

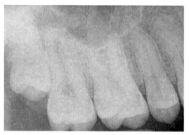

X-Ray of Sally's wisdom tooth

At that first visit, I gave Sally a QuickSplint® as it was likely her long-term splint, which she hadn't brought with her, needed adjustment.

The oral surgeon was recommending a Botox injection, but I felt that was just dealing with the symptoms, not the underlying cause, so I asked Sally to return to me for further assessment.

She'd been wearing the QuickSplint for a week and was beginning to feel somewhat better. I adjusted her long-term splint.

Two days later she returned for another splint adjustment and reported that she was no longer in pain, but her husband had told her she was snoring more when wearing the splint.

This brings us to the main point of this story.

I thought Sally was coming in for a minor adjustment to her splint—something that would just take a few minutes—but with the mention of snoring, and knowing that her palate narrowed towards the rear, I was concerned that airway issues could be present and those could be serious. Sally needed to understand how her decision not to have the surgery was affecting her overall health and I needed to make time to help her see this.

Fortunately, my assistant was able to take care of the splint-fitting for my next scheduled patient so I spent the next 30 minutes assessing Sally's Mallampati Score (a screening tool for the throat), having her look at her throat with me with a hand-held mirror, showing her the BiteFX sleep apnea animation and explaining the interrelationships of her palate geometry, CR, muscle relaxation and breathing.

I encouraged her to consider all the variables—those she had control of (such as weight, opting for surgery) and those she didn't have control of (like genetics). I told her: *"You deserve to take care of yourself. Your daughter deserves a mother who feels fantastic! You're worth it—you were made by God!"*

Over the visits Sally knew that I had listened to her concerns and registered what was going on in her life. She also knew (from observation) that I had made space in a busy schedule for her.

The words of Sally's response,

"I really appreciate you taking the time,"

only hint at what I observed in her body language and demeanor.

She had gotten the message, was acknowledging her responsibility to make the right decisions for her health, and considers me as a trusted advisor as we move forward together with a plan that supports her healthy decisions.

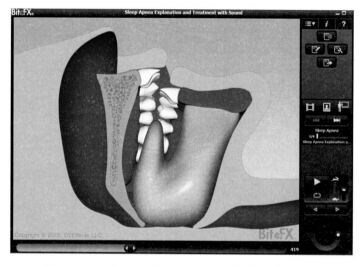

Sleep apnea animation showing tongue blocking the airway

2.
Never Prejudge People's Ability to Accept Comprehensive Care

Do you look at somebody that might have scraggly hair and soiled clothes and pre-judge them thinking inside, "They'll never afford my fine dentistry"?

At a fundamental level this is another way of saying "I don't care"!

My favorite counter-example of this is a young man named Neil who came to my practice several years ago.

Neil had long hair and dirty clothes— not too surprising as he was a rock mason and just came off the job.

In his hand he had some stone models of his upper and lower jaws. There were

Neil on his first visit

about five or six teeth on top and six or seven on the bottom. As he was talking I noticed that they looked like pretty good teeth.

Neil told me that he was supposed to get a denture.

I looked at him and laughed and said, *"Neil, I bet you woke up this morning and thought 'Oh boy I just can't wait to get all my teeth pulled and get some plastic stuck in my head!'"*

Neil answered: *"I don't want a denture! I want teeth - teeth that don't come out! I want those teeth that don't come out and have screws in under them."*

Just looking into his mouth with a rather cursory exam and without the benefit of x-rays, I told Neil we could save his remaining teeth with some crowns and fillings, and he could have what he wanted with dental implants as I saw that he had adequate bone levels.

He said: *"That's what I want, and I know they're expensive; how much will this cost?"*

I then performed the quickest estimate of treatment ever by knowing it would require 12 implants, hygiene care and crowns and replied' "About $60,000 dollars".

Neil's response was immediate acceptance, with just one question:

"Do I have to pay all at once upfront?"

I replied: *"We'll have a lot of work to do together and it will take time. Please pay half when we begin and the balance when you're done and we're both satisfied with the outcome."*

This transpired before I looked at his x-rays or performed a complete exam. Never judge a book by its cover!

Here's how Neil looked afterwards—quite a different picture!

The lesson? Find out what people really want!

Neil 18 months later

- Had I prejudged Neil and only proposed what I thought he could afford, he'd probably have gone to a different dentist and certainly wouldn't have received from me the dentistry he really wanted.
- What I proposed was what I heard he wanted and what I knew was the solution I'd have wanted myself.
- Following these principles richly rewarded both Neil and me!

Strategy in Action— Never Prejudge!

Dr. Brian Gray

Brian Gray, DDS, Washington, DC

The lesson of not prejudging is reinforced to me almost every week. Here are a couple of recent examples.

Decided Not to Age Discriminate!

John was a long-time patient of mine who beat the hell out of his teeth over the years. I'd explain to him that we could do things to repair the wear and prevent future wear, but he kept on kicking the can down the road content to leave things as they were and probably telling himself that they weren't going to get any worse.

A year or so back, he came in for his periodic visit and, sure enough, his teeth were further worn down with about a third of the original length left. By this time, he was 80, and I was thinking, *"Brian, don't be silly here, there's no way John wants to invest money in his teeth when there are so many other things he can do with it in his last decade or so!"*

However, I bit the bullet and decided I should stick to my principle of always presenting the best to my patients. This time I had BiteFX and was better able to show him visually what was causing the wear and (at last!) he responded: *"You were right—my teeth are wearing down!"* I showed him what would be required to repair his mouth—some crowns and some bonding—that would come to a total of around $20K.

John said, *"OK. I want to do it!"* I must have looked surprised as John confirmed, *"Yes, really! This is work I believe we should do!"*

It would have been so easy for me to assume John would continue kicking the can down the road and to not bother taking the time to explain what was best for him. That would have been an expensive reallocation of the 15-20 minutes it took to go through it all with him! Glad I didn't do that!

African American, Divorced, Single Mom, Late 40's—Don't Think She'll Invest $35K In Her Dental Health!

Monica came to me not too long after a painful divorce. Long term effects of occlusal disease were evident with splayed, missing, and broken teeth.

Hearing her story and imagining what her financial position might be I was strongly tempted to give her only the lowest cost options.

However, experience and a personal commitment to always tell my patients what is best for them, lead me to tell her how teeth could be straightened with Invisalign, repaired or replaced with crown and bridge, and set up for longevity with appropriate attention to her occlusion. The cost would be $35K.

"I want to do it," was the response, *"No more letting things go! I am determined to get myself back into full health."*

It felt good to know I helped Monica make this step of self-respect—and it only happened because I had the courage, or the well-ingrained lesson, of treating her with the same respect afforded to all my patients.

3.
Don't Just Talk About What You Know; Let the Patient Know How You Feel!

At the core of this strategy is a single concept I learned long ago from the clinical psychologist Charles Sorenson PhD. He told me:

> *"All of our help is at the feeling level not the cognitive or knowledge level."*

That might sound like a lot of gobbledygook, but it gets down to this:

> *"Patients respond to what they pick up from our feelings much more than what they learn of our knowledge!"*

Dentists are the only people I know that routinely try to overcome patients' feelings about dentistry and their mouths with LOGIC.

Suppose someone comes into your office with a mouth that is failing. Our natural desire and expectation is to give them all the facts, spell out the logic and likely consequences of their condition, and trust the patient to make the rational decision to select the best treatment plan they can afford.

Unfortunately, that's NOT the way it works.

We *do* need to give them the facts, the rational explanations of why things are happening, and the likely consequences (as you'll pick up from many of the other tips in this book), but unless those explanations are sprinkled with the **"magic dust"** of feeling, all that logic and knowledge is wasted!

Sprinkling this magic dust probably involves an attitude adjustment along with changing or adding a few words—you'll give the same explanations but from a slightly different perspective!

For the attitude adjustment, you need to knock out your tendency to be solely rational by focusing on how you feel about your patient.

Give yourself a few minutes to picture the worst outcomes for your patient if their issues are not treated—broken or missing teeth, gum issues, ugly or hidden smiles, decreasing self-confidence, and compounding issues of ill-health. Will you feel good about letting them take that path? Of course not!

Now picture the best outcomes: beautiful teeth, wonderful, confident smiles, great health, and eliminated past chronic issues. How's that going to make you feel?

You might want to write down these thoughts, so they're captured, collected, and well-phrased.

Now, when you talk to the patient keep your feelings in mind and include some of them as you communicate your findings.

Tell them that you feel really *badly* about what's happened (or happening) to them. That you would like an opportunity to *help them learn how* to stop this crazy endless dentistry syndrome. That you have skills that can help the whole person, not just their teeth.

Tell them that you will *feel badly if they continue to fail while they're on your watch.*

Include the elements that will bring you the greatest satisfaction, such as helping the patient achieve their dental goals, put past issues behind them, and feel positive about their smiles.

No need to go over the top! Keep it real! Just let your patients see and hear how you feel about them and their treatment.

I find the opportunities for expression are endless, magical, and one of the things I enjoy most about dentistry. I hope you have the same experience!

Strategy in Action—Let Patients Know How You Feel!

Dr. Alan Blondman

Alan Blondman, DDS, New York, NY
It's 40 years since I graduated from dental school, 35 years since my wife, Randi, and I (call us crazy) set up our private practice in New York, and I'm still excited to be practicing dentistry and gaining new insights into what it means to be excellent.

Perhaps it was our upbringing, I don't know, but right from the start Randi and I wanted to serve our patients in a way that would make them feel they were an extension to our family. We clearly succeeded in doing this since we have a long list of patients who have been with us for decades, many multi-generational families of patients even to the extent that, in the near future, I expect to welcome the fourth generation of one family to sit in my chair. And now, my son Max has joined our practice!

What did it take for us to do this, and was it worthwhile?

I can't put a dollar value on it—though anyone who is having to market their practice to bring in new patients might quickly give you a several-thousands-of-dollars-per-month figure that I'm not spending. Of much higher value to me is the respect I receive from my patients and the satisfaction I have of knowing I'm delivering life-long care to them, my friends.

How we did it—through a combination of two attitudes:

- Always seeking, to the best of our ability, to understand the nature and causes of dental diseases and how to treat them;
- Having a desire to communicate through education and concern, our desire to bring our patients' well-being to a higher level.

Through our words, our posture, and our actions, our patients learn how we feel about them. They know we care about their health, so they stick with us and choose options that optimize their health.

Let me tell you about two different patients Joe and Cecily.

Joe is a long-time patient of record. He has always been diligent about home care and makes his continuing care visits like clockwork.

Joe was a learning experience for me (not a position you really want to be in as a patient!), but he stuck with me because of the foundation of feeling and care established over the years.

Several years ago, he started having issues with one of his rear right molars—#2. Tell me if this sounds familiar to you! First, it needed an inlay, then a crown. Then the crown broke, so I did it over. Then it broke again, and I fixed it again. Then the adjacent tooth broke so I fixed that. Then problems started to occur on the left side, with breakages and a tooth having to be extracted.

By the end of this years' long sequence, I had been through the Pankey Institute training, so at each stage, I was ensuring his occlusion was in harmony with CR. However, contrary to my expectations, that wasn't halting the deterioration.

Finally, I took a step back and looked at his face. It was incredibly asymmetrical! Time for more learning!

So, I went back to my Pankey guys and consulted with a prosthodontist and an oral surgeon. They all agreed: you've got to look at Joe's TMJs!

An MRI confirmed Joe had a degenerative joint on the left-hand side—and prompted Joe to recall a trauma received years before.

With the root cause established, a grateful Joe was able to choose how he wanted to move forward.

Cecily came to our practice a year or two back and needed a bunch of work. Money was an issue, but I still proposed the care I felt she needed. I didn't push, I never do, just explained the issues with the aid of BiteFX, and what it would take to resolve them. She went away for months, but then she came back.

While reviewing her issues and breaking down her options, she made the comment, *"My bite doesn't feel right."* Sure enough, on reviewing her models, I could see that a small adjustment could make her feel more comfortable. She agreed to the treatment and immediately said, *"That's so much more comfortable!"*

She could see, and now feel, that I cared about her best interests, so we've started a comprehensive care case, staged to meet her budget.

That's my every-day life—sharing with people what's best for them, letting them know my concern for their entire well-being, and giving them the space they need to decide they're ready to act.

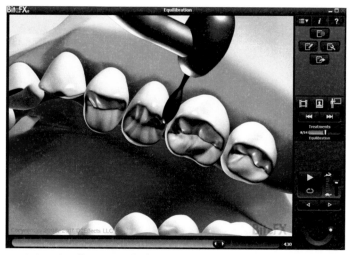

Animation illustrating the bite adjustment (equilibration) process

4.
Beware of Only Explaining Occlusion When You Encounter a Severe Occlusal Case

A number of courses in dealing with occlusal issues conclude by going into complex cases in which many teeth have been lost or damaged and prompt the question:

"Where on earth am I going to start with this case?"

The purpose of looking at these cases is to show that following the recommended steps, which work towards establishing a healthy occlusion, makes the problem manageable.

I think this causes some dentists to return to their practices thinking that the occlusal principles they've learned only apply to complex cases. This is the only explanation that makes sense of the wide range of numbers of occlusal issues we hear BiteFX dentists encounter.

While some dentists say,

"I'm not using BiteFX much as I don't see many patients with occlusal issues,"

others tell us,

"80% to 90% of my patients have occlusal issues, so I use BiteFX with everyone!"

They can't both be right, can they?

I'm in the camp that sees many occlusal issues and have found that it pays big dividends to make all my patients aware that having a healthy occlusion is one of the factors I look for and aim to establish for them. It sets me apart from other dentists they've experienced, helps them place a higher value on my services, prepares them for any issues I diagnose, and makes them educated sources of referrals.

A story related to me by Dr. Peter Dawson had a big impact on my thinking in this area.

A wealthy patient came to him from the middle-east and recounted that she had had her mouth reconstructed several times. Each time the dentist had told her,

"By reconstructing your mouth, we'll be able to solve your problem!"

Obviously, they didn't solve it!

Early in the interview process, this lady told Pete,

"If you rebuild my mouth again to solve my problem, I'm going to sue you!"

To the best of my recollection Pete said to me,

"How do you think I'm going to treat that viper?"

Most of us would say, "Don't touch her! You'll be bitten badly!"

His answer was simple, but impactful:

"I'm going to treat her like everyone else - do a complete exam!"

And that's what he did.

She had no slide whatsoever but a simple prematurity on one of her back molars. He complemented her on her excellent reconstruction, then proceeded to adjust one back molar so both sides hit at the same time in centric relation.

 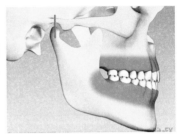

A back tooth being adjusted so that teeth hit evenly on both sides

The woman **felt relief immediately from there on** and, no doubt, paid Pete well for the treatment.

What this taught me was never to categorize my patients as "occlusal patients" and "non-occlusal patients". Whether occlusal issues are obvious or not, I assess the state of their occlusion and determine the right course of treatment from there. A tiny, virtually invisible, occlusal discrepancy can drive patients to distraction.

- If I want to deliver the best, I have to assess everyone's occlusion, and consequently, I believe that everyone is better off if they have a basic understanding of what occlusion is about.

Strategy in Action— Beware of Only Explaining Occlusion in Severe Occlusal Cases!

Dr. Dennis Stiles

Dennis Stiles, DDS,
Gaithersburg, MD
Private Practice Owner,
Diplomat of the American Board of Dental
Sleep Medicine, Faculty of UMD Dental School,
Serves on the Board of Directors of the Pankey Institute

A Dental Whodunnit!
(Or in this case: whatdunnit)

What do you do when a patient comes back to you feeling like their bite is off?

I know I had too many of these situations in my early years of dentistry. They drove me crazy but also inspired my search for answers that, when I found them, greatly enriched my life as a dentist.

I'd like to share a situation I recently encountered to trigger your problem-solving skills.

- First can you identify what drove a dentist from a nearby community crazy, and

- If you can do that, what is the best way to communicate the solution to the patient without disrespecting your colleague?

Lucy came to our practice recently having decided, from researching her symptoms on the web, that she had a bite issue which would best be diagnosed by a dentist with a T-Scan machine. Our website mentions we have a T-Scan (a machine that reads bite forces between teeth). A few months earlier Lucy had gone to her dentist with a broken molar (#30) and had agreed that she needed a crown. However, when the crown was fitted it made her bite feel uncomfortable.

At the crown delivery visit her dentist made some adjustments, was happy with the occlusion of the new crown and sent Lucy off to see how it felt over the next few days.

Well, it didn't feel good. Things weren't comfortable on the right of her mouth. In fact, Lucy said:

"I can only feel my teeth hitting on the right side."

. . . so she went back to her dentist for him to fix her issue.

Now put yourself in the shoes of this dentist.

What did you change? The crown on #30.

She was feeling comfortable with her bite before the crown was put in, and after the crown was in, she suffered discomfort.

What should you do? Adjust the crown on #30.

Because she was uncomfortable with her new bite, the dentist saw her six times over the following weeks, continuing to make adjustments on the new crown. It ended looking like this:

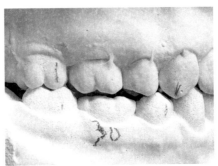

Model showing the heavily "adjusted" #30

That should have done it, wouldn't you think?

BUT, as you know because Lucy came to me, this didn't fix Lucy's discomfort and she still felt she was only hitting on the right side.

Her dentist told Lucy there was nothing else he could do. The patient reported that she was told:

"It's all in your head."

. . . as he had ensured that the change he had made was not a contributing factor.

SO . . . What did the dentist (or we, if you were following the above logic) miss?

Lucy's problem was that she had a pre-existing occlusal issue that she had adapted to. #30 played a part in that adaption. We don't have the original #30 or a record of how it occluded but we'd probably have seen that it shared the bite force with other teeth on the right side in a manner that Lucy had become used to and considered to be comfortable. #30 probably broke because it was taking more force than the other teeth, but it was what Lucy was used to. Perhaps the temp replicated Lucy's comfortable occlusion or was close enough, but the crown certainly didn't. Suddenly things changed, and Lucy's proprioceptive capacity informed her that her teeth were no longer coming together in the old "comfortable" manner. The occlusal problem had always been there, and Lucy had learned to tolerate it, but it was now annoyingly apparent.

From this point onward, it would be impossible to fix her issue by adjusting the crown on #30—unless we magically could recreate her old touch points, but even then, the continuity of feeling had been broken, so Lucy felt unhappy because she was only hitting on the right.

How do I know this is the answer?

A. At the Pankey Institute I learned how to do a comprehensive exam including mounted study casts, and am thankful for that.

B. I guided Lucy's jaw into its fully seated position (often called "centric relation" or "CR"), saw that in this position her teeth only hit on #31 and #2, and the teeth only found the position in the above picture after the jaw came out of its fully seated position. I took a record that allowed me to replicate the CR position on the mounted study casts.

C. Lucy immediately felt comfortable when I gave her a splint that had multiple even contacts when her jaw was fully seated.

Now to the second part of the whodunnit:

- Having perceived the likely answer to Lucy's problem during the pre-exam interview, how would you communicate your findings with her, without commenting on the other dentist?

I'll tell you my approach, but it will be more instructive if you pause here and jot down the key words, phrases or questions that you'd use.

Here's what I said:

"Lucy, as you suspected we are dealing with an occlusal issue that your dentist was not aware of. Would you like me to explain how the bite system works? (Yes)

Let's start by looking at your models.

See how I can manipulate the model to make your teeth come together just like you do? Do you notice that, with the models mounted in this device (an articulator), your teeth first come together at one point, then I need to slide them into your normal bite?

That's because your bite system is designed to work like a tripod— two 'feet' of the tripod are your condyles which are stable when fully seated in your jaw joints; the third 'foot' is your teeth which should all touch at the same time.

What you're seeing is that when your condyles are seated, your teeth come together at a single point, on your right side—which is going to feel much more pressure than it wants to feel. Your muscles therefore trigger and bring the condyles slightly out of their sockets so that more teeth can come together with the pressure more evenly distributed.

In its current state, your system is imbalanced—you either have your condyles seated, with all the pressure on one tooth, or your condyles are unseated with the pressure spread across more teeth.

That didn't happen because of your new crown—this imbalance existed before the old tooth broke and the crown was fitted, but you'd grown accustomed to it, and perhaps the old tooth played a part in making things feel comfortable or comfortable enough. The new crown was different, and your teeth are so sensitive to even the smallest changes, you suddenly became aware of the imbalance that existed before.

Does that make sense?"

At this point I assess if that explanation is enough for the patient, indicated by their response and body language (which says, "I'm with you, what's next?"), or if they need more explanation, often the case if they're more technical, want to grasp all the details and have questions. If they need more details, I whip out my Microsoft tablet with BiteFX and let them see the bite system in action. If they don't need more details, I move on. Lucy didn't need more detail, so I proceeded with two of my favorite questions:

"How often would you say you are putting your teeth together?"
and

"Why are you putting your teeth together?"

I ask these questions as it makes people think about what they're doing with their teeth. Deciding not to clench or bring the teeth together frequently is a component of helping their bite system to relax.

I went on to explain what an occlusal splint would do and to construct one for her. She liked how it felt.

Lucy came back three days later for a (pre-arranged) adjustment, reporting that she loved the splint, as it made her bite feel so much better. I checked that the splint had not introduced any sleep issues (it hadn't) and made a couple of minor adjustments.

Only when I'm confident we've relaxed her muscles and stabilized her system will we get into details of making that stable bite permanent, with new bite record, new models, a trial equilibration and replacing the ground-down crown. I'm confident Lucy will want all future dental work to maintain her stable bite!

It's because of cases like this that I believe that I have to consider **the occlusal health of all my patients**. If I don't do that, I open them up to suffering from problems that were hidden in the past because I change something else that brings that problem to the surface or I leave my work exposed to the destructive forces of occlusion should a change of circumstances, stress, or habits make them start clenching or grinding.

My patients understand why I do this and appreciate me taking this additional care. I hope you get to experience the benefits of delivering occlusal health to all your patients!

Doing the Opposite—Explaining Occlusion to Everyone!

Here's a tip that I've learned from a mass of dentists who are using BiteFX with the greatest success:

Explain occlusion to everyone!

Why would you take your valuable time to do this before you've examined the patient when you may have no idea whether they have any occlusal disease?

I've concluded there are several good reasons to do this:

1. You have an expertise and understanding that **few dentists in your area can match.** Isn't it a good idea to make sure that ALL your patients know you're different?

2. Once a patient understands and appreciates that occlusion is a critical component of their dental health and that you know how to give them a healthy occlusion, **do you think they'll ever be satisfied going to another dentist who doesn't have**

your expertise? (Even if they don't have any occlusal issues right now.) I don't think so!

3. You've **increased the patient's perception of your value** long before you talk to them about the cost of your treatment. You may charge more than the dentist down the road, but you're worth it!

4. Certain aspects of your exam are going to be different from anything the patient has experienced before. **They'll be much happier** if you give them a basic understanding why you are attempting to seat their condyles BEFORE you take hold of their jaw!

5. **Patients are going to be curious** about your assessment of their occlusal health:

   a. Are their joints fully seated when their teeth come together?

   b. Do they have good anterior and lateral guidance?

   c. Are their molars showing signs of premature wear?

   They'll be on your side when you explain your findings!

6. If they have occlusal issues that should be treated, they **won't be surprised** when these come to light. Because they understand a healthy occlusion is important to the longevity of their teeth, they'll want you to fix the underlying causes of their problems. With the right pauses, you'll find they'll be asking you what the solution is!

7. When your patient talks to a friend who is suffering some of the symptoms you described as possible indicators of occlusal

disease, **they're likely to recommend that the friend pays you a visit**. They certainly won't do this, or even remember, if you haven't given them that basic occlusal understanding.

The dentists who are doing this tell us they see up to 25% growth in their revenues.

Here's an example of what one dentist, Dr. John Cranham, shows to his patients during his pre-exam interview. Notice that it's simple and only takes Dr. Cranham two or three minutes to present:

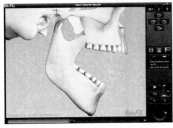

1. How the jaw and TMJ work

2. How the muscles wor

3. What ideal tooth
contacts look like

4. Why you want to see
peaks-to-valley contacts

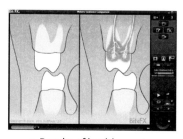

5. Results of healthy canine guidance (left) and unhealthy (right)

Strategy in Action— Explaining Occlusion to Everyone!

Dr. Alain Aubé

Alain Aubé, DMD
President, Canadian Occlusion Institute

"There's A Lot of Crying in My Office"

The impact of explaining occlusion is so profound that it would be madness for me not to spend the 5 to 10 minutes that I do with every patient.

Every day I hear:

"You're the first person to explain this to me!"

"No one has ever taken the time to show me this. Thank you for taking the time!"

Do you think the patients who say this to me are going to go to another dentist? Never!

For such a small investment in time (greatly helped by BiteFX, I have to say—it saves me much saliva!), I reap big benefits. It's not just the revenue this generates, considerable though that is, but it's the boost I get from these grateful comments and the relief I see in patients' eyes when finally they know what's causing their pain and they've found someone who understands. There is HUGE SATISFACTION in that. If you're not experiencing it now, you need to!

There's a lot of crying in my office. Many of my patients have been in pain for so long, perhaps fearing they have cancer, or having been told by other professionals who have been confounded by their pain that they're crazy, that they experience overwhelming relief on finding the answer. Tears are a natural outflowing of this relief and the joy of hope.

Let me tell you about Catrina who came into my office the other week.

Catrina is a lovely, beautiful girl in her mid to late 20's who came in with her father—rather unusual for someone her age; I'll tell you why in a minute. She had her Panorex in her hand.

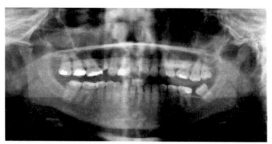

Catrina's Panorex

She told me how she'd been having terrible headaches for a long time but they were getting worse, so bad that she had gone into the emergency ward at the hospital a week earlier. They couldn't figure it out, despite taking the x-rays, so they told her: *"You don't have a problem! It's in your head! Move on! You're taking space that someone with a real problem needs!"*

Can you believe it? Unfortunately, Catrina took that message to heart and concluded that the only way to relieve her suffering was to take her own life so attempted suicide. Thankfully, she failed, but that's why her father was with her that day—he was desperate to find a solution for his daughter.

Within seconds of looking at the Panorex I could see that half of one of her condyles wasn't there so I said, *"I know what your problem is, and you'll be able to see it in the X-ray yourselves in a couple of minutes' time!"*

Catrina looked at me and I could see in her eyes a mixture of disbelief and hope. Disbelief that her problem could be so quickly diagnosed. Hope that my confidence was well-founded and that relief was in sight. Her father's eyes echoed her feelings, and he voiced their thoughts: *"We can't read X-rays!"*

Encouraged by my confidence they both sat down and watched attentively as I took them through my standard spiel of using BiteFX to show them a healthy open and close motion with muscles, then the TMJ going through different stages of deterioration, concluding with the tooth and muscle relationship controlled by the nerves.

I then handed them the Panorex, and they both exclaimed, *"Oh my god! How did no one else see it?!!"*

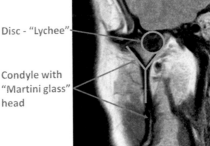

Disc - "Lychee"

Condyle with "Martini glass" head

MRI of her disc and condyle

Catrina had fallen off her bike at the age of 7 and still had a mark on her chin from that fall. This had precipitated the condylar issues so that she had no cortical bone and, uniquely, her disc was rolled up in a ball within the head of the condyle—like a lychee in a martini glass!

I gave her a flat plane splint, and her headaches were resolved.

The solution would have worked without my explaining the anatomy and function of her masticatory system, but I hope you can see the difference those few minutes made to Catrina, her father, and me. They didn't have to cross their fingers and hope they could trust me to fix Catrina's issue. She wasn't going to resist my proposed treatment, nor is she likely to discard her splint because it was just a "coincidence" that her pain was resolved when she first wore it. Also, her stress was removed because she saw with her own eyes what the problem was. What other issues might that stress have caused had I not taken the time to help her understand?

Do yourself, your patients, your staff, and your practice a big favor and take the time to explain the origin of their problems to all your patients!

5.
Know That Patients *Will* Come Back Later to Hear Your Studied Findings

It's a false belief that patients won't come back later for a consultation!

I know it's a common mental issue that you need to get the patient to schedule dentistry the first time you examine them.

I can tell you from experience that that's a lie! Don't believe it!

I simply tell a patient:

"Mrs. Smith, as I've been learning about your mouth; taking photographs and x-rays; checking your jaw muscles, your jaw, and your palate; observing your grinding, and looking at the cracks and broken fillings, I really need time to study and gather my thoughts, so I can explain what I see and recommend the same to you as I would if it were me in the chair.

"So, if I could have your permission [showing mutual respect for them], *I know you have a busy life like the rest of us, but I'd like an opportunity to have you come back where we can just sit and talk and have a conversation and you can learn and see what I've learned about you."*

Patients have no cultural reference point for a doctor giving that much time and attention, so are highly receptive to the offer.

Try it! It works!

Strategy in Action— Patients Will Come Back!

TJ Bolt, DDS, Omaha, NE

"A Well-Considered Approach Makes You the Trusted Solution Provider That Patients Return To!"

Dr. TJ Bolt

Very often these days it seems that patients are coming to me for a second or third opinion. They've visited other medical professionals, but their issues haven't been resolved or they just haven't felt confident in the solutions proposed. This can include dentists who never looked for occlusal problems (occlusal disease is the #1 undiagnosed dental disease) and dentists who recognized occlusal issues but went ahead with treatment plans without checking for TMJ stability.

The reason these patients are coming to me is that all these other professionals, whether they be neurosurgeons, physiotherapists, orthodontists, chiropractors, or MDs (primary care or ENT), have been treating the patients' symptoms, not the root cause of those symptoms. Naturally if you're just treating symptoms and not dealing with the root cause, the problems are going to continue happening.

As you can imagine, these patients are more than a little wary of what they're going to be told, having lost trust in the medical establishment. My biggest challenge, therefore, is to establish trust with that patient.

I know my diagnosis is going to be accurate, that my recommended treatment will be the right one to address their issues, and that it will be executed with excellence—but how do I help the doubting patient, who may have been mishandled for years, come to understand and believe these facts?

Basically, I follow a consistent, well-considered approach that lets the patient see that I care, that I understand the causes of their problems, and that I am the one they can trust to deliver. Here's an overview of my approach:

I **always** have an interview with the patient before my evaluation (exam).

Then the stages are:

- RAPPORT—During the interview we are sharing ideas, communicating "I like you," "You like me", I first listen to the patient, then ask if I can share my story (which describes how they've been trapped in a disease-focused, problem-solving cycle from which they won't escape until the root cause is addressed).

- ENGAGEMENT—Having established rapport, I use the animations in BiteFX to engage the patient's attention and understanding. Invariably this is the **first time** a doctor has explained anything to the patient **before** doing stuff!

- Every stage is important, but I hope you can see that I'm already distinguishing myself from the other medical professionals the patient has dealt with.

- CONNECTION—**I ask their permission** to do my evaluation. It's a simple request but it is amazingly empowering to the patient, letting them know I'm not jamming my expertise down their throat; and it makes a valuable connection between me and the patient.

  Because my evaluation involves elements they won't have experienced before, I again use BiteFX animations to help the patient understand why I do what I do.

- COMMITMENT—After my evaluation **I always make another appointment** to discuss my findings. This gives me time to work up models, confirm my diagnosis and make sure I'm going to present my thoughts to the patient coherently. During this second appointment the patient will see that their problems aren't self-correcting; that they need to make a decision to stop the progression of the disease.

- CO-DEVELOPMENT—Now that the patient understands their problem and its cause, and has seen that solutions are possible, I work with the patient to develop a plan that fits their needs, budget and desired timescales.

Take Sue, who recently came into my office, referred to me by a local physiotherapist.

Here's how my approach worked for her:

- RAPPORT—As always, we sat down to chat before I did any physical examination. I listened to what she had been through. Sue told me that she'd been treated by a dentist who had identified a premature occlusal interference and provided an occlusal splint. However, she had destroyed that splint, so the dentist decided he couldn't fix her problem—it had to be stress/muscle related so sent her to the physiotherapist. Fortunately, I've shared the BiteFX animations with that physiotherapist, so he knows the types of symptoms I can help with. When he saw his treatments weren't working, he knew Sue should come to me.

  Having listened, I asked if I could share my story, which I call "The Dreadful Story" and you can see an example of that in the webinar I presented: www.bitefx.com/hero-dreadful-story

- ENGAGEMENT—As I went through my story, Sue was starting to relate the causes I was talking about to her symptoms. I had her attention and full engagement as she began to see there was hope that someone understood what was going on.

- CONNECTION—When I asked Sue if she would permit me to perform an evaluation (later that week—as I didn't have time the day she came in), it was a pleasure to observe and hear her response. First there was that partly surprised look, that a doctor was asking permission to examine her; then an adjustment of posture as Sue said to herself, "He respects me! He is giving me control!"; then the words, "Of course! I'd really appreciate that!"; and best of all that hard-to-describe feeling that she and I had a connection, a mutual trust and respect that will be the foundation of a long-term professional relationship.

- COMMITMENT—After the evaluation and during the follow-up appointment, Sue saw the confirmation that I understood her problem and asked what to me is the vital question: "So what would you recommend we do about this?"

- CO-DEVELOPMENT—We went through the treatment plan of creating a splint, how we'd adjust it as the jaw settled into a stable position, how we'd wait until that position was verified over several visits, and then how we'd replicate the comfortable bite of the splint in permanent restorations of her teeth.

  Sue wasn't able to sign-up for the full plan there and then but was happy that we could start on the first stages that would bring her pain relief knowing that the later stages could follow when her budget would allow.

This approach works for me every time, and I never have issues with patients saying they can't come back for the later appointment to discuss findings.

You have answers they need to hear! Be methodical, be confident, and share what you know, and patients will follow your lead, give you time to provide them well-considered answers, and value your services highly!

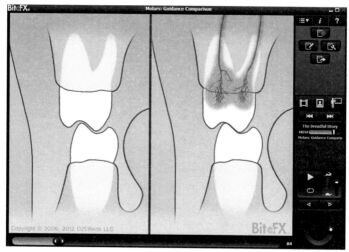

One of the animations used by Dr. Bolt in his "Dreadful Story"

PART 2

Timing, Presentation Tools, and Techniques

*With the right principles established in Part 1,
here are ways to tune the details of what you do.*

We consider frequency, duration, tools, tailoring, and techniques!

6.
Sow Early "Occlusal Seeds"

Do you have a pre-exam interview with your patients—face-to-face without the patient feeling vulnerable and cowed in the dental chair?

This is so important for a number of reasons:

- You let the patient know you are interested in what concerns them.
- You gain clues on things to look out for in your exam.
- Taking this time communicates "I care" even if it's just a few minutes.
- You distinguish yourself from other dentists who are in such a rush to "produce" that they see any time spent away from a patient's mouth as lost cash.
- You show that you're a thinking dentist—one who sees a bigger picture than a single broken tooth or problem pain.
- Last but not least, you have the opportunity to open the eyes of your patient to the importance of occlusion in their dental health—what I'm calling "sowing early occlusal seeds".

When I sow early occlusal seeds with every patient:

- My patients know I'm different; I understand critical factors and am an expert in an area they haven't encountered in other dentists. Even if they don't have an occlusal issue on this visit, they're much more likely to stick with me in the future as they don't want to go to a dentist who doesn't understand occlusion.

- The patient is prepared for me doing things in my exam that they haven't experienced before. They can connect my actions with the basics I've explained to them.

- When we discuss my findings after the exam, they're not surprised by the mention of an occlusal issue—they expect me to tell them about their occlusal health.

- If I mention some of the possible symptoms caused by occlusal issues, the patient is equipped to be an informed referral source—if they hear a friend or relative describe a symptom, they may well say, "You know, my dentist mentioned he can often help people with that symptom. You should see if he can help you!" Again, they know I'm different, so it makes sense to recommend me rather than a run-of-the-mill dentist.

My recommendation:

- **Sow early occlusal seeds by taking two or three minutes with every patient to show them the basic concepts of occlusion and explain that you'll be assessing their occlusal health as part of your exam, so expect a few different tests than they've experienced before!**

Strategy in Action— Sow Early "Occlusal Seeds"!

Dr. Kelley Brummett

Kelley Brummett, DMD, Newnan, GA

Serves on the Board of Directors of the Pankey Institute and Visiting Faculty for the Essential 3 course

Understanding Takes Time to Develop

Have you ever gone into a patient during their hygiene visit, told them something like *"You're showing signs of bruxing"* with the patient responding, *"You're right!"* and had your hygienist later say to you, *"I said the same thing, but the patient didn't believe me"*?

This often happens with patients. Although my hygienists don't like it, we have all come to understand there's a learning process going on with our patients. This learning sometimes takes time.

The hygienist shares a discovery with the patient, something new, different, or that they'd rather not hear. The initial reaction is to resist or deny, and that's what our hygienists hear. The patient then sits and ponders the new information, perhaps unconsciously, and starts to think, *"That's not unreasonable,"* *"That might be possible,"* or *"Actually, I do do that!"* Then, when I come along, and they hear the statement a second time, they are predisposed to accept it.

With this observation, that it often takes time for a new concept or understanding to take root, my hygienists now take the lead in sowing the seeds of occlusal understanding. They are the ones who:

- First, ask the questions:
  "Do you suffer from regular headaches?"
  "How often do you bring your teeth together?"
  "May I do a quick muscle exam?"

- Then, use BiteFX to introduce muscle function and hyper function, occlusal causes of abfractions, and the reasons we aim to deliver occlusal health to all our patients. (I'd say they utilize BiteFX better than I do!)

- Finally, encourage the patients:
  "Let me know if you notice anything between now and your next visit"

When the patients return and share with us about the things they are now noticing, they'll often jibe, *"You made me think about this!"*

That's true, but as we're bringing to light destructive forces which, if left untreated, would cause greater damage over time and lead to expensive restorations, the patients are always grateful that we "made" them think!

Because my hygienists sow those occlusal seeds of understanding early, they make my job easy.

By the time I'm talking to the patients they've already internalized the concepts, accepted what is going on in their mouths, and want to know what they can do to change the destruction. All I have to do is recap what they've already been told to confirm we're on

My hygienist talking to a patient about a splint

the same page, pick up any questions they have, and move naturally into the next steps of treatment planning.

7.
Do Not Take Too Long Explaining Occlusion!

Dr. John Cranham

John Cranham, clinical director of The Dawson Academy, makes two apparently contradictory statements:

"Many of my patients understand occlusion better than the average dentist . . ."

And:

"Less is more—you've got to be careful not to bore your patients to death by telling them too much!"

How can his patients understand occlusion better than the average dentist if Dr. Cranham is not taking considerable time with them to explain every detail?

The answer is twofold:

1. The sad fact is that the bar is set low—the average dentist is pretty confused about occlusion, so it doesn't take long to raise a patient's understanding above the average.

2. He uses a great tool (BiteFX), so patients quickly see things that the majority of dentists haven't seen.

Whether you have one great tool to help you explain occlusion or are using a combination of tools (e.g. skull, TMJ model, patient's models, pictures and sketches), the challenge is the same:

- **Make sure your explanation isn't so long or so detailed that you lose your patients' interest.**

Your patient usually just needs to know what is normal, and how they deviate from normal, perhaps with the consequences if no action is taken. Then, they'll ask for a solution, and you can give it to them!

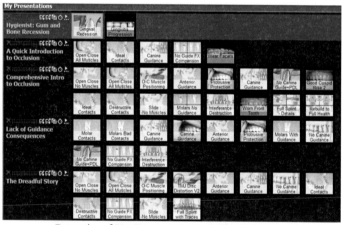

Examples of BiteFX presentations. These can be as short as a couple of items (e.g. "Gum and Bone Recession" at top), or as long as you make them! However, keep your focus and only tell the patients as much as they need to know to make an informed decision!

Strategy in Action—Don't Talk Too Long!

Dr Eric Farmer

Eric Farmer, DDS, Wichita, KS
Director of Professional Development
at Clinical Mastery Series

Going from a Dissertation to Bare Essentials Made the Difference for Long-Time Patient

It is very hard not to give a dissertation on anterior and cuspid guidance. This is where a BiteFX animation can speed things up, showing what happens when the cuspids get burned off and the destruction that occurs. A picture (animation) is worth 1000 words—and it's quicker!

Mrs. Jones, a 50-year-old lady and long-time patient of mine, had worn her incisal edges unevenly but she was really not interested in doing much about it.

At that time, we talked about how the front teeth protected the back teeth and showed her with a mirror how that was affecting her asymmetrical wear. I spent 30 minutes trying to give her a PhD in occlusion rather than telling her the solution which would result in her having straighter and whiter teeth.

Now, while it was important for her to understand on some level why it was happening, I took too much time in the why and how and did not place enough emphasis on the end product. With straighter/whiter teeth, she would not speak with her hand in front of her face.

Ten years later I finally got to do her smile. One of the questions I ask patients when they finally accept treatment is: *"Why now?"*

The answer typically revolves around a crisis like a big chip in a front tooth and the understanding that something must be done, or multiple failing bondings on front teeth where they just do not last more than a year or, obviously, an important event coming up like a wedding or reunion.

Mrs. Jones's *"Why now"* was: she had been taking care of an ailing relative for 5 years, and now, it was time to do something for herself (and, of course, I'd explained things to her in a way that didn't send her running for the door!).

8.
Equip Patients to Explain What You Offer to Their Friends!

In a way, this is another advantage of not just explaining occlusion when you encounter severe occlusal issues, and of sowing early occlusal seeds, as described earlier.

Basically, if your patients:

- Don't know you're an expert in occlusion
- Don't know that a healthy occlusion matters
- Don't have any understanding of what occlusion is or why it matters
- Don't know some of the most common symptoms of an unhealthy occlusion

. . . there's no way they're going to suggest to friends and family that they might benefit from visiting you!

I'm NOT suggesting you add a "Here's how to identify and refer patients to me" spiel!

I AM suggesting that there are indirect benefits to educating your patients about occlusion and giving enough thought to a standard introduction that you share with everyone, that you'll remember to tell them why occlusion is important and give them two or three symptoms that they should care about and might hear about in others.

Problems I like to mention:

- How even a small occlusal discrepancy can cause people to have an uncomfortable bite, grind their teeth, and develop regular headaches because of over-worked muscles—and they can suffer from these problems for years because no one realizes it's a tooth issue! (Remember Dr. Dawson's "viper lady" story I shared in secret #4?)

- How repetitive tooth or restoration failures often have an occlusal cause.
- How lost canine guidance can open the door to total mouth destruction.
- How gum and bone recession, or loose teeth are also indicators of occlusal problems.

I don't go through this list all at once, but tag each issue to my explanation of how healthy looks. So, I'll show them with the help of BiteFX:

- Here's how teeth should come together. Here's what it looks like if they don't all come together at the same time. And that's why someone might work their jaw so much that they grind teeth away or strain their muscles resulting in regular headaches.
- Here's how people avoid an initial contact. Here's what happens when they're sleeping (they hit on that contact). And that's why restorations built to their comfortable bite can keep breaking!
- Here's healthy canine guidance. Here's lost canine guidance and how that allows rear teeth to hit, loosen, bend and break.

It's easy and natural, and I can't keep count of the number of people who come to see me because a friend or family member mentioned to them that I might have expertise that can help them. I even had one family in Incline Village, Nevada, refer both their daughters from Manhattan to me—so remember that you have expertise that not many people encounter! When patients know this, they can share that good news with others!

Strategy in Action— Equip Patients to Explain What You Offer to Their Friends!

Dr. Ian Buckle

Ian Buckle, BDS,
Thornton Hough, UK
Director of the Dawson Academy UK

Tell Your Patients the Stories You Want Them to Tell Others

As dentists, we too often "hide our light under the bushel"—we're just not good at telling others what types of dentistry we like to do.

What I've found and what I teach is that if I tell my patients about the types of dentistry I like to do and then ask them to tell their friends, they do!

Here's how it works.

As part of my full exam, I ask my patients about the usual things —teeth, gums, cancer, bite, smile—and I usually get some interaction with them on these topics. If this reveals, or if I find, an issue, I deal with it. But perhaps nothing applies, or the patient isn't ready for treatment. I'll follow-up on one or more of the items we've discussed with a comment like:

"That's an area in which I like to help people" or
"That's one of the topics I teach to other dentists" or

DON REID, DDS & DOUG BROWN

"Treating that (whatever it is) is one of the strengths of our practice"
or

"We like to deal with occlusal issues,"
followed by:

"If you have any friends or colleagues with this problem, you might suggest that they visit us because we'd love to help them."

You'll be surprised at how often the patients do just that. I'm amazed at how often it comes back word-for-word what I told the patient.

My patient, Nick, is a great example of this. It was clear that Nick's smile needed some work, so I brought it up with him while chatting about the results of my exam and asked if he'd like to do something about it. Nick, however, was quite happy with his smile, so he didn't want to do anything. That's his choice, which I always respect.

As usual I said, *"No problem Nick, but I do enjoy giving people great smiles—it's one of the strengths of our practice—so if you have any friends or colleagues who are looking to give themselves a better smile, you might tell them that we're the place to go."*

Two weeks later Mark comes in. He tells us that he and his wife were having dinner with Nick and his wife a couple of days after I'd seen Nick. Get this! The *wives* were talking to each other and Mark's wife makes a comment about wishing Mark had a better smile. Nick's wife responded, *"He ought to go see Nick's dentist as he likes to do that stuff!"* Nick had actually told his wife that I liked doing smiles, and she had given the referral!

Mark needed some lower ortho work and 10 veneers—about 10,000 pounds ($13,000) worth of dentistry. Not a bad result from a simple request that took me a few seconds to say to Nick!

Remember—tell your patients the stories you want them to tell others!

9.
Make Sure You Are Able to Show What Will Happen If Action Is Not Taken!

We need to help people to connect the dots. We want them to understand what healthy occlusion looks like and how they might have an unhealthy or destructive occlusion. Then, the vital conclusion is to show them the sorts of things that might happen if they don't take action to re-establish health or use something like a splint to slow or halt the destructive effects (more wear, more breakage, continued headaches).

It might seem obvious to us that an untreated issue is going to lead the patient down the road of increasing issues, but it's not obvious to the patient, or they may just close their mind to the potential consequences because they don't want to think about them.

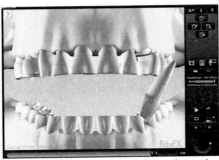

Extreme consequence: a destroyed mouth

It's our duty to forewarn them!

By offering to treat the cause of their problems we become the patients' friend. It may cost them in the short-term, but long-term they'll be avoiding the much higher costs of bigger crowns, more crowns, root canals, tooth removals, implants, gum and bone disease, full mouth restorations, and the like.

Of course, I don't give them this long list as they would think I'm a scare-monger. Instead, having identified an issue, I'll walk them through: here's what healthy is; here's where you are; here's what can happen if we take no action (and fixing those issues later on is going to be expensive). I'm matter-of-fact and objective, and I stress that I want the best for my patients.

Explaining the consequences is most easily done with an animation that shows the progression of destruction, but it can also be done with the right photos and verbal explanations to make sure the patients connect those dots!

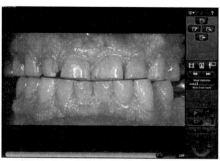

It happens!—Photo of a destroyed mouth.

Strategy in Action— Show What Will Happen If Action Is Not Taken!

Dr. Rick Rogers

Rick Rogers, DDS, Frederick, MD

The Right Visuals Save Me Time and Enable Decisions

About 10 to 15 years ago, after practicing dentistry for several years, it became obvious to me that the issues I was seeing with my patients' bites and TMJ's needed visual illustrations. What was going on was too complex for me to explain with words, sketches on a dry-erase board, and 2-D models. Some of these concepts are hard enough for dentists to grasp, let alone trying to convey them to patients!

One of our dental assistants was an artist, and she drew pictures for us that showed problems like disc displacements and arthritic changes. The drawings were highly beneficial and made a big difference in my patients' ability to understand problems that they couldn't visualize. This led to them, in most cases, to proceed with my recommended treatment.

Several years later, along with many technological advancements, we started to use a 3-D computer animation software called "BiteFX." This software depicted the same scenarios I was showing with my artist-drawn illustrations but with more details and greater visual impact. Our patient's learning accelerated, so it saved us time, and we saw improved case acceptance.

TMJ damage and pathology are not limited to the adult population. In pediatric cases, we use animations to explain to the parents, so they have a clear understanding of the diagnosis. Some TMJ pathology leads to facial deformation, and the child will have little or no symptoms. Parents are often unaware of the condition affecting their child's proper facial development. After using 3-D animations for parental education; we will then have them look at their child's face and ask them to tell us which side the problem is on. They invariably get it right!

Lindsay, a 9-year-old girl who has been my patient from birth, is a good example of this. She recently came in for her regular appointment with our hygienist. In response to some standard questions that our hygienist asks; Lindsay reported that her left TMJ was clicking and that it had been clicking for a while.

When I went in to look at Lindsay, I confirmed the clicking on the left TMJ and observed that her facial growth was being impaired on the same side. This is most likely due to the left condyle not growing at a normal rate and the subsequent impact on the ramus and other growth areas. The right side had normal growth, and the left side was showing signs of limited growth. This is most easily observed when looking at the patient's chin. It will begin to deviate to the side with limited growth.

I then met Lindsay's mom in our consultation room and showed her a 3-D animation that depicts slow condylar degeneration in an adult and subsequent facial deformation. I explained that Lindsay's situation was similar in that, although her left condyle wasn't shrinking, the facial deformation was the same due to its restricted growth. With the animation, I was also able to show how things could progress if the problem wasn't resolved—with a greater canting of the jaw and likely adaption of the maxilla to the cant of the jaw. Clearly not a desirable future for a 9-year-old girl.

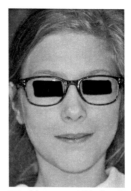

Would you spot Lindsay's condylar problem?

Seeing Lindsay every day, her mom hadn't noticed the gradual changes. Then when Lindsay joined us, having completed her hygiene appointment, I asked her mom what side she thought Lindsay's damaged TMJ was that was causing growth changes and facial deformities. She immediately said, *"On the left"*—confirming that she understood what a shorter condyle on one side looked like and, equipped with that understanding, she was now able to see in Lindsay what she hadn't noticed before.

There was no doubt her mother clearly understood when she then asked, *"Can we take action now to see if that jaw growth can be brought back to normal?"*

From my early clinical experiences, I know that I'd have really struggled to get that positive acceptance had I not had a 3-D visual aid. It not only helped me show Lindsay's current condition, but it also let me show future facial changes if no action was taken. Being able to show the likely future progression of an untreated damaged TMJ is such a game changer. It's not just words coming from the mouth of the dentist predicting doom and gloom. The patient or parent now has the visual comprehension and can see for themselves a situation they don't want to experience!

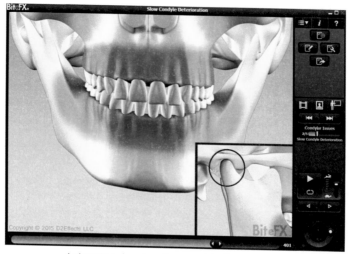

Animation showing slow condyle deterioration

PART 3

Bringing The Strategies To Life

We've shared with you the top tips and techniques that can make a huge difference for you, just as they have for hundreds of other dentists.

Perhaps it will be enough for you to take the one or two tips that made the most sense to you or are the easiest to apply immediately.

However, for those who want to think about putting it all together to see a major impact on their practices, you need to understand why BiteFX makes such a difference when it comes to implementing the strategies.

Tool That Made the Biggest Difference for Don

See if What Works for Him Can Work for You

Don writes:

From the first day I started using the prototype animations we were producing for what became BiteFX, I saw lights come on in my patients' eyes.

It was like going from night into daylight.

Before I had the animations, I'd get knots in my stomach when I saw patients' eyes glaze over during my occlusal explanations.

With the animations it became almost pure joy—the enthusiastic nods, the expressions of thanks for explaining their issues, the downhill road to gaining treatment acceptance, all combined for a transformative effect on me and my practice.

Don using early versions of BiteFX with patients

Since then, BiteFX has evolved to be a sophisticated but easy-to-use presentation tool with a much-expanded set of concept-enlightening animations.

BiteFX helps me, and hundreds of other dentists, put all these tips together:

1. When I open patients' eyes to the importance of occlusion and they see I understand, it reinforces to them that <u>I care</u>.

2. Having standard presentation templates that I tailor to individual patients reminds me to *offer comprehensive care to everyone.*

3. Because people very quickly understand the concepts communicated in the animations, I spend less time telling them what I know and *spend more time telling them what I feel.*

4. Sharing a few basic BiteFX animations is fun and becomes a habit, so *everyone hears about occlusion.*

5. BiteFX gives me confidence that patients will have a good experience when they return to go into the details of my diagnosis. Consequently, *I believe they'll want to come back for that second appointment*—and they do!

6. With BiteFX, I can explain a few key occlusion concepts incredibly quickly, so it's easy to *sow "occlusion seeds" early.* It's never a waste of time and always part of my "I care" message.

7. There's so much in BiteFX that we have heard of some dentists falling prey to the temptation of giving their patients a full lecture on all they know about occlusion. A little bit of forethought and planning should be enough to avoid that

trap! Customizing a presentation with the right set of animations and pictures for a particular patient (a quick and easy process with BiteFX) should ensure that you *never take too long explaining occlusion.*

8. If you don't understand something, you have to rely on rote memory to explain what you were told to others. Most of us have very poor retention of material we don't understand. However, if you see a picture (or better, a moving picture) that makes you say, "I get it!" that concept generally stays with you for life.

   Patients who see the BiteFX animations have that "I get it!" experience, so they retain the understanding of the main points and *are well equipped to explain what you offer to their friends.*

9. Some of the most popular animations in BiteFX are those that show the consequences of problems being left untreated. *Seeing what will happen if action is not taken* is a big motivator for patients!

BiteFX helps me apply the well-tried principles I've shared with you.

When you understand how to treat bite problems from the simplest to the most complex, working with occlusion becomes like a playground: fun, intuitive, and easy! My greatest joy comes when I hear a patient say, *"I'm so glad I found you, where have you been all my life?"*

That can be your daily experience too!

Other Dentists Rate BiteFX

You shouldn't take just our word that BiteFX is a great tool—we helped in its creation, so we're bound to be biased!

Here are comments from just a few leading dentists who use BiteFX:

Dr. Janet Burthem

Janet Burthem, BDS, St. Asaph, UK

"BiteFX is the perfect tool for explaining why occlusion is fundamental to providing successful dentistry.

It is very rare that a patient declines occlusal treatment once they have watched a demo using BiteFX, as they can instantly relate their own situation to what they are watching.

It is invaluable to our practice."

Dr. Hal Stewart

Hal Stewart, DDS, and co-founder of the The Stewart Center for Minimally Invasive Dental Medicine

*"This software is so vital in helping me move my patients forward that **the cost is irrelevant compared to what it does for my practice** and my patients."*

Dr. Chris Toomey

Chris Toomey, DDS, Towson, MD

"When faced with tough budget decisions, BiteFX would be the absolute last thing we would cut from our practice.

I would rather sell my car then get rid of BiteFX."

Dr. Peter Dawson

Peter Dawson, DDS, and founder of The Dawson Academy

"BiteFX will help everyone in your practice understand *your commitment to eliminating the destructive effects of occlusal disease.*

Its potential for helping you enhance your communication of key occlusal concepts is exciting everyone at the Dawson Academy."

Dr. Alain Aubé

Alain Aubé, DMD, and president of the Canadian Occlusion Institute

"I tell all my students they need BiteFX for patient explanation.

*I explain to them that **it literally sells at least a case a day."***

Dr. Michael
Schuster

Michael Schuster, DDS, Scottsdale, AZ Founder and CEO of The Schuster Center for Professional Development

*"Mal-Occlusion is the **un-diagnosed and untreated disease** in dentistry.*

21st Century dentists who take a 'systems approach' to oral and systemic health would greatly benefit by incorporating BiteFX into their everyday co-diagnosis and treatment planning with their patients."

Dr. Margareta
Gavrila

Margareta Gavrila, DDS, Chino, CA

In my practice of restorative, reconstructive dentistry, BiteFX is just as important as the face bow, articulator, or radiographs. BiteFX is an important tool for communication with my staff, patients, interdisciplinary team-orthodontist, periodontist, endodontist, and oral surgeon.

What BiteFX Is Not!

BiteFX is not a cure-all for all your patient communication issues. . . . There may be some bad habits or relatability issues you're going to have to work at! BiteFX may, however, become the core support as you address those problems.

BiteFX is not a set of videos you leave your patients to watch. . . . It's a tool to help you and your staff explain concepts to your patients. Patients seeing and hearing you explain these concepts has infinitely greater power than them watching an anonymous narrator on a video!

BiteFX is not able to help improve the quality of your dentistry. . . . We doubt that you'll have read this far if you are not able to deliver high quality results to your patients. We trust you will always strive to deliver dentistry that is compatible with the concepts BiteFX helps you communicate!

BiteFX is not static. . . . The BiteFX team is constantly working to widen and deepen the animations it provides, keep it current with the latest operating systems and enhance its features and usability for our members. When you become a BiteFX member, know that the team wants to hear from you because your input will make a difference!

***BiteFX is not* for all dentists.** . . . Although the range of what BiteFX covers is always expanding, occlusion understanding is at its core. If occlusion isn't important to you, BiteFX may not be the tool for you.

However, if you want to be numbered with the best, becoming a BiteFX member is the place to be!

Reasons to Keep Doing What You're Doing

We hope that you can see the value of each suggestion in this book, from each of the 9 strategies to the use of BiteFX.

In conclusion, we'd like to address some general and some product-specific reasons people decide not to change what they're doing and hopefully give you that bit more incentive to take the steps you need to bring you the same success and enjoyment of dentistry that Don and all the other dentists who have contributed to this book experience every day!

So . . . what might keep you from stepping forward?

You don't want to change

Did you expect to read this book and not change anything you do? We think not. Change usually takes effort and usually is worth that effort! If fear of change is a real problem, get yourself started by writing down the steps you want to take, order them from easiest to most difficult, and start with what is easy. Congratulate yourself on each change made and use that as motivation to take the next step!

You're happy with your current results

You wouldn't have picked this book up if that were the case, so either you didn't like what we shared, or you just don't want to take the effort to make the changes!

We're sure they'll take less effort than you fear, and you can only learn from the experience of trying new techniques!

You don't have time

Are you so busy that you can't make room for working on the changes that will enable you to free up more of your time?

We hope it's clear to you that you're going to have to find some time to escape from your busyness, or else it's going to dominate the rest of your (short, stressful—sorry but that's the truth) life.

One great piece of advice Don took to heart when he was running ragged was that he didn't have to reform his whole way of working or his whole schedule; changing one method, action, or activity he did, or determining one patient would be given the full exam, was sufficient to initiate the changes that in the long-term lead to a transformed practice.

You don't want to be too successful

We're all likely to say, "That's ridiculous! Of course, I want to be super-successful!"

Perhaps we're getting too much into the psychoanalytical here, but if you have a history of trying different ways of moving forward, of growing, but none of them seem to work, you might want to explore whether you have programmed yourself, your unconscious brain, for limited success.

Do some self-analysis with the help of one of the classics like Napoleon Hill's "Think and Grow Rich," Stephen R. Covey's "The 7

Habits of Highly Effective People," or Norman Vincent Peale's "You Can If You Think You Can"!

You don't see many occlusal issues

Most of the dentists quoted in this book would say that 80% to 90% of their patients have signs and symptoms of occlusal disease.

If they are right, what are you missing?

Perhaps you are only looking for much bigger occlusal issues than they are—those complex cases often featured at the ends of (or throughout) occlusion classes? Those complex cases are shared to demonstrate how an understanding of occlusion can guide you; they are not intended to be the only cases in which you apply the principles!

Take another look and learn from the dentists in this book how you can distinguish yourself and elevate your dentistry by identifying, explaining, and treating even the smallest signs of occlusal disease. You will be surprised at how many patients greatly appreciate your attention to detail.

You don't have the support of your staff

If your staff are negative about the occlusal principles you want to implement in your dentistry, they likely don't understand what it's all about.

We've been surprised by how many dentists come back to us, after their staff have attended a couple of hour-long BiteFX Quick-Start coaching sessions, excited by the change of attitude in the staff members. The coach was focusing on how to use BiteFX, but the staff were focusing on the animations that suddenly made things clear to them!

Make sure your staff have had the benefit of seeing for themselves what may have taken you months to truly grasp! Fortunately, the BiteFX animations make the learning process much faster.

You think BiteFX costs too much

BiteFX only costs too much if you pay for it but don't use it!

Each use of BiteFX can make the difference in a patient deciding to opt for your suggested treatment or choosing a fuller solution than they might otherwise have selected. The return on each use can be from 10 to 500 times the monthly cost. Most dentists use BiteFX several times a day; many tens of times a month, so the monthly returns are a hundredfold and up.

Use BiteFX and enjoy these returns, so you'll agree with Dr. Hal Stewart that "The cost is irrelevant compared to the benefits it brings my practice."

You believe that a software product like BiteFX should be sold for a one-time price

That's not an unreasonable perspective and we certainly started with a one-time pricing model. However, we found that keeping the software vital and growing, in the way our customers expected, required a different pricing model. We are constantly developing new animations to extend the range of concepts dentists can communicate with BiteFX. Microsoft and Apple continually enhance their operating systems (Windows and iOS (for the iPad))—if we don't keep up with these changes, the BiteFX software stops working. We need to keep challenging ourselves to see if we can make BiteFX easier to use and easier to learn or provide new functions (such as touch screen support). We need to keep our users informed, supported, and updated, while marketing BiteFX to new generations of occlusally-aware dentists.

The only way to do all this was to switch to a monthly payment model, so several years ago, we decided to make that change.

Our decision proved to be a good one and is the reason BiteFX exists today and can offer you the transformative experience described in this book.

The good news for you is that the monthly pricing model brings you two big benefits:

1. Your cost of entry is much lower—you can see if BiteFX works for a fraction of the price we'd be charging for a one-time pricing model.

2. You only pay us if BiteFX is working for you. If it's not working for you, you stop paying. If it is working, you'll consider the monthly payment trivial compared to the benefits your practice is reaping.

It's not a convenient period for you to take on a new product

If this is the case (and you're not just making an excuse to put off a life-changing decision to another day!), set a date now for when you believe the inconvenient period will end—e.g. when your office remodel is completed, your new computers installed, or when you will take control of your calendar and not be controlled by emergencies! Put a reminder in your calendar on that date to put BiteFX into action for you, your staff, your practice, and your patients!

Frequently Asked Questions About BiteFX

Over the years we've come to know the most common questions asked about BiteFX, so we thought it would be most helpful to give you the answers right here!

What can BiteFX do for my practice?

Those who follow the strategies described in this book report 10% to 25% increases in their practice revenues (on top of the small amounts paid for BiteFX).

An unexpected effect for many practices has been that simply involving staff members in the BiteFX QuickStart coaching sessions opened the eyes of the staff to occlusion. They changed from barely willing helpers to whole-hearted supporters.

What concepts/issues does BiteFX illustrate?

There's not enough space to list all the concepts that you can communicate effectively with BiteFX but here's a list of the major themes:

- Healthy occlusion
- Destructive occlusion
- Muscle function
- TMJ and condyles
- Tooth contacts
- Bruxing effects

- Abfractions, fractures, worn teeth
- TMD
- Diagnostics (leaf gauge, articulator, classifications)
- Treatments (splints, equilibration, rebuilding)
- Sleep apnea
- Condylar deterioration
- Restricted envelope
- Implants
- Gingival recession

Should I customize my presentations to each patient?

Yes and no! Your brief introductory, pre-exam presentation and some common topics will be the same for everyone. When you are explaining your exam findings that are likely to lead to extensive treatment plans, it's worth taking a few minutes to tailor the presentation to that patient and include some of that patient's photos. With BiteFX this is a quick drag-and-drop operation.

Why are there no narrations with the animations?

BiteFX is designed as a clinical tool; one with which you, or your staff, does the explaining. This communicates to your patients that you are the experts and allows for quicker, more personal explanations as you can see when the patient understands a concept and move on to the next point.

How long does it take to learn to use BiteFX effectively?

That largely depends on your confidence with computer software.

Many dentists see a 5-minute demo of BiteFX at a conference and are using it effectively on their first day back at the office.

Others prefer some coaching and practice using BiteFX a few times themselves before using it with patients.

Our recommendation is to keep it simple—you don't have to be a master of every feature. Pick a few animations you like, and start using them tomorrow! You can learn all the details later when you're ready to take advantage of them.

Can my staff use BiteFX?

Absolutely!

It's up to you to determine what's most effective for your practice. We'd suggest keeping some explanations to yourself as the communication with your patient has a high value—if your staff do all the explanation with you rushing in and out to "seal the deal" or answer a few technical questions, your patients will feel you don't care personally about them. However, as long as you structure things so that the "I care about you" message gets across, go with whatever fits best for you and your staff.

Does anyone use BiteFX to talk to other medical professionals—GPs, orthodontists, for example?

Yes—they report this can greatly enhance the understanding of occlusal concepts and the effectiveness of communication.

GPs can become great sources of referrals once they understand how you can help certain patients with chronic pain symptoms. BiteFX on the iPad can be a great tool for these exchanges, perhaps during a meeting over coffee or lunch.

Why do you charge a monthly membership?

Maintaining software on ever-evolving operating systems such as Windows or iOS, providing excellent, responsive support, and continuing to expand the breadth and depth of animations requires continual investment. Having a monthly membership is the best way we've found of ensuring BiteFX is the best it can be now and into the future.

Also, a monthly membership provides a low cost of entry. If you use BiteFX regularly, following the strategies described in this book, you'll find that the monthly membership is trivial compared to the benefits it brings. If you are not using BiteFX, it won't do anything for you, and you can cancel your membership—saves you paying thousands of dollars for the product only to find you leave it in the box!

How often are updates issued?

Currently we issue new animations about once a month. The updates are easy to install, and you can set BiteFX up to install the updates when you exit BiteFX, and they install in seconds—so updates never interrupt your use of BiteFX.

You can also choose to ignore the updates until you are ready to use them or see that must-have new animation.

Why attend the monthly webinars?

We broadcast monthly Insiders' Secrets and Tips webinars that are free to Platinum members, with other members being given the option to purchase seats (with access to recordings) for individual webinars.

We invite top-notch dentists who present topics of relevance to BiteFX members. Those who attend the webinars tell us they are highly stimulating, giving them insights into new techniques or advances that they'd otherwise have missed. You can ask questions directly to the presenters and gain a sense of being in a community of high-end, occlusion-aware dentists.

Can I use BiteFX when presenting to other dentists?

Yes. We just ask that you acknowledge BiteFX in your presentations and let attendees know where they can find out more about BiteFX if they are interested.

There are two or three different ways of integrating BiteFX animations with your PowerPoint or Keynote presentations. We'll be happy to explain those to you when you start preparing your presentation.

What return can I expect on my investment in BiteFX?

This depends on the value of dentistry that you offer (is your average case $1,500 or $15,000?) and how closely you follow the strategies described in this book.

At the low end, we expect you'll see hundredfold returns (each $1 spent on BiteFX will generate $100 for your practice). At the high end, that could be $250 for each $1 spent or more.

What does it take to cover the cost of using BiteFX?

For most dentists, a low treatment plan is in the $1,500 range and profitability from 20% to 40%. Therefore, just one additional treatment plan per month more than covers the cost of BiteFX. Even the time saved in explaining occlusion to one or two patients can cover the cost of BiteFX.

And most BiteFX members tell us they use BiteFX several times a day, attributing at least one new treatment plan acceptance per day to BiteFX. You'll find the cost is trivial compared to the benefit!

How can I become a BiteFX member and have the BiteFX animations and software in my practice?

See the offers on the next few pages for options to either explore BiteFX further or become a BiteFX member immediately and make it work for you!

Do you provide any guarantees?

Absolutely!

We back BiteFX with a full 6-month, money-back guarantee.

Unless you and your patients absolutely love it, we'll pay back the money you've paid us! In fact, we've decided to improve on the guarantee with the Heroic Offer you'll see a few pages ahead.

Also, our cancel-any-time policy acts as a guarantee for you that you won't need to pay for BiteFX unless it is working for you!

PART 4

PUTTING IT ALL TOGETHER—
THE NEXT STEP

*You've learned the strategies
that can establish you as your patients' hero.*

*You've read how BiteFX is the perfect tool to give energy
and meaning to each of those strategies.*

*Here's an easy way you can see for yourself that the
BiteFX animations, pictures, software, support,
and services will work for you.*

Heroic Returns on Your Investment—Guaranteed!

Don't sit on what you've learned in *Becoming Your Patients' Hero*! Bring the strategies to life by taking the BiteFX 60-day test drive!

We believe you'll see *truly heroic returns* on your investment—we're talking about bringing in *50 to 100 times the BiteFX membership fee* in new income each month. We think you'll be hard-pressed to find a better investment!

Demonstrate to yourself that the strategies work.

We guarantee you'll be *overwhelmingly satisfied with BiteFX* and its ability to help your patients, or we'll stop billing immediately and you keep the welcome gifts.

Why would we do this? We don't want you to pay us unless BiteFX is working for you, and we know it can produce huge returns.

Go to www.bitefx.com/hero-offer for the full details.

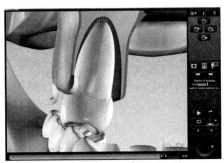

Conclusion of a popular animation
showing how lack of canine guidance
can lead to an abfraction

ABOUT THE AUTHORS

Dr. Don Reid

Dr. Don Reid earned his BS in Chemistry at UCLA in 1974 and dental degree at Temple University in 1978. He served as an enlisted Marine in Vietnam in 1968 and a Naval officer from 1978-81. After practicing in a remote desert town from 81-96, he moved to Lake Tahoe and established Tahoe Dental Artistry in 1996. Don's focus is adult esthetics and restorative dentistry, implant surgery, and sleep dentistry with an emphasis on occlusion or a comfortable stable bite.

Don is a graduate of the Dawson Academy, Piper TMJ Institute, and Misch International Implant Institute. He's a long-standing member of DOCS, and past affiliations include faculty club member at Spear Education, staff selection consultant for Gallup, and AACD member.

Don was awarded Fellowship status with the International College of Oral Implantology in 2002.

As a founder of the Academy of Microscope Dentistry, microscopedentistry.com, Dr. Reid's use of a dental operating microscope for routine dentistry enables him to perform his 'Art' with a degree of precision attainable from magnification.

He co-created and developed BiteFX, which is being used in 40 countries to help dentists and dental students understand the complexities of bite problems which cause headaches, sore jaws, teeth grinding, and unnecessary tooth loss.

Don lectures throughout the USA and internationally to assist his colleagues in gaining the confidence and skills to solve the universal problems caused by bad bites.

Don and Marilyn Reid

Don's roots are from humble beginnings growing up in rural Pennsylvania. His dad sold potato chips and mom was a waitress. They never had a prolonged vacation as money was scarce, but the family was full of love and encouragement. Don was the first in his Russian immigrant family to attend college.

Don and his wife, Marilyn, have four daughters and one son. These children have given them the gift of 11 grandchildren.

Don and Marilyn are active Tahoeites enjoying, mountain biking, hiking, downhill and cross-country skiing, boating, and fly fishing. Their greatest enjoyment comes from serving one of Marilyn's gourmet meals in their Tahoe home to family and friends.

Doug Brown

After graduating with a degree in Mathematics from Cambridge University, England, in 1977, Doug had his eyes opened to powerful ways of teaching math while taking a Postgraduate Certificate in Education at Exeter University, England, a couple of years later.

Doug's thoughts on communicating concepts continued to evolve during his career in computer software development. This took him from being a programmer for a UK bank in the early eighties, to an assistant vice president position for an international software company by the mid-nineties, and consultant to the software division of a large computer manufacturer through 2012.

In 2001, Doug founded Dynamic Thought®, LLC with the goal of using animations to help people grasp concepts that had been mastered by experts who were visual thinkers. Several prototype animations were created to prove the idea worked covering a variety of concepts that included the database query language called SQL, skiing, and the complicated offside rule in soccer. These animations proved that the idea worked—those who saw the animations said, "That's the best explanation I've seen of that topic!"

When Doug met Don three years later in 2004, the Dynamic Thought team of animators, software developers, and graphic designers (all working part time), were ready to act on an idea that had significant business potential. Asked whether there was anything in Don's dental practice that could benefit from animations, Don responded with a resounding, "Yes" since he was struggling to communicate occlusion effectively to his patients.

With that, Don joined forces with Dynamic Thought to create BiteFX (under the auspices of the new joint-venture company "D2Effects LLC").

The Brown Family—Numbers 1 thru 7!

Since then, as CEO, Doug has lead the design and creation of the BiteFX animations, software, systems, memberships, and webinars, along with the general management of the D2Effects company (which does business as BiteFX LLC). He has been working full time in this position since 2012.

Doug is the proud father of three boys, one daughter and one daughter-in-law, here showing-off the sweaters given to everyone by youngest son, Ben (Brown #6), who is also a member of the BiteFX team.

Doug lives with his wife, Liz, and Brown #6 in Truckee, CA where he is active in his local church, enjoys cross-country (which feels like up-hill) skiing, volleyball, hiking and biking in the summer, and a certain amount of gardening (to humor Liz's passion).